# CLASSIC GLACIAL LANDFORMS OF

# SNOWDONIA

This guide is dedicated to all my geological friends in the Welsh RIGS groups and, in particular, to Stewart Campbell and Margaret Wood of the Countryside Council for Wales.

*Kenneth Addison*

I love its strand and its mountains,
its castle near the woods and its fine lands,
its water meadows and its valley,
its white gulls and its lovely women.
'Exhultation'
– *Hywel ab Owain Gwynedd* (d. 1170)

CLASSIC GLACIAL LANDFORMS OF

# SNOWDONIA

**KENNETH ADDISON**
**School of Applied Sciences, Wolverhampton University, and St Peter's College, Oxford**

*Series editors*
Rodney Castleden and Christopher Green

Published by the Geographical Association
in conjunction with the
British Geomorphological Research Group

THE GEOGRAPHICAL ASSOCIATION

THE BRITISH GEOMORPHOLOGICAL RESEARCH GROUP

# PREFACE

Some elements in the landscape we see around us are very ancient; some change very rapidly, almost while we watch. Landscape scientists (geomorphologists) can explain these landforms, and the processes that make them, but much of their work is published in specialist journals and is therefore not available to the general public. It is one of the aims of this book to make up-to-date explanations of the most striking and interesting landforms in England and Wales accessible to all. These classic landforms are naturally of interest to geography students, both in school and university, and we hope that the style and format of this series of guides will make them easy to use both at home and in the field. We hope that a clearer understanding of the origins and dynamics of landform development through time and space will help both student and visitor to maximise their appreciation and enjoyment of the landscape.

Encouraged by the response to the first edition of the *Classic Landform Guides* we are pleased to introduce this new edition. The relevant maps for the area covered in this book are the Ordnance Survey 1:50 000 *Landranger* sheets 115 (Snowdon) and 124 (Dolgellau); refer to the Ordnance Survey map index for coverage at 1:25 000. The British Geological Survey also publishes a series of new geological maps which complement much of the content of this book. They include the 1:50 000 sheet 106 (Bangor) and seven 1:25 000 sheets of the mountain areas (see Bibliography).

**Rodney Castleden** *Roedean School, Brighton*
**Christopher Green** *Royal Holloway, University of London*

© the Geographical Association, 1983, 1997
As a benefit of membership, the Association allows members
to reproduce material for their own internal school/departmental use,
provided that the copyright is held by the GA. This waiver does not apply to Ordna
Survey mapping, questions about which should be referred to the Ordnance Surve
ISBN 1 899085 24 6
This edition first published 1997
Published by the Geographical Association, Solly Street, Sheffield S1 4BF. The vie
expressed in this publication are those of the author and do not necessarily
represent those of the Geographical Association.
The Geographical Association is a registered charity no. 313129
*Cover photograph:* Snowdon from Capel Curig *Photo:* Ken Addison
*Frontispiece:* The Llanberis Pass in winter *Photo:* Ken Addison

# CONTENTS

**Acknowledgements**
The Geographical Association would like to thank the following organisation for
permission to reproduce material in this publication:
The British Geological Survey for the map of Wales at 1:250 000 scale on
page 8, reproduced by permission of the Director, BGS. © NERC.
apping reproduced from Ordnance Survey 1:50 000 Landranger mapping with the
permission of The Stationery Office © Crown Copyright 82324M 09/96.
*Copy editing:* Rose Pipes
*Illustrations:* Paul Coles
*Series design concept:* Quarto Design, Huddersfield
*Design and typesetting:* Armitage Typo/Graphics, Huddersfield
*Printed and bound in Hong Kong by:* Colorcraft Limited

# INTRODUCTION

## Geological background

Snowdonia bears profound testimony to two cataclysmic periods in the development of British landscapes. Submarine and terrestrial volcanic eruptions, accompanying oceanic sedimentation and other igneous activity, laid the geological foundations for North Wales during the Cambrian and Ordovician periods over 435 million years ago. These Lower Palaeozoic rocks were deformed later during the Caledonian tectonic (mountain building) episode. The rocks survived subsequent total denudation, owing much to their great mechanical strength and, after localised tectonic elevation in the Tertiary period, formed some of the extensive upland plateaux in Britain prior to the **Quaternary** 'Ice Age' (Figures 1 and 2).

During the past 1.6 million years, a procession of some 20 cold stages with associated permafrost or glaciers interrupted by short temperate stages, such as the present **Flandrian** stage, have

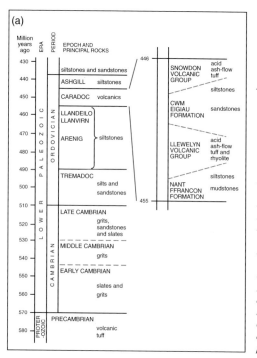

*Figure 1: Timescale of principal geological events in Snowdonia.* The Lower Palaeozoic timescale (a) (left) covers the formation of underlying, hard rocks dominated by marine sediments of the former Iapetus Ocean and Caradoc-age volcanic and plutonic rocks in the mountain core. Igneous activity was associated with the Caledonian orogeny. The Quaternary timescale focuses on (b) (opposite) Snowdonia's Late Pleistocene history, about which most is known. Temperature changes refer to °C above or below the present.

dominated global Quaternary environments. It is impossible to ignore the dramatic impact of intense **Pleistocene** glaciation in transforming the high Tertiary plateaux of Snowdonia. Glaciers occupied deep mountain recesses (**cirques** or cwms) until only 10 000 years ago, marking their limits with irregular mounds of debris (**moraines**) eroded from their rock basins. Traces of these glaciers are still fresh and relatively little altered, but they were the smallest of ice masses. Beyond their limits, at an altogether larger scale, lies evidence of earlier ice sheets approaching 1000m thick, burying all but the highest peaks and eroding deep valleys which now isolate separate mountain groups. The growth and decay of glaciers in Snowdonia *twice* during the most recent, **Devensian**, cold stage can be traced with some confidence and earlier glacial episodes hinted at (see Figure 1).

It was a geological and religious heresy to propose a glacial history for Britain 150 years ago. Geology was an infant science, and few British geologists had seen a glacier. Yet Snowdonia's glacial landforms are so impressive that after 1840 they were in the vanguard of the emerging *glacial theory*. Many famous scientists have walked the ground covered in this book, among them Charles Darwin before

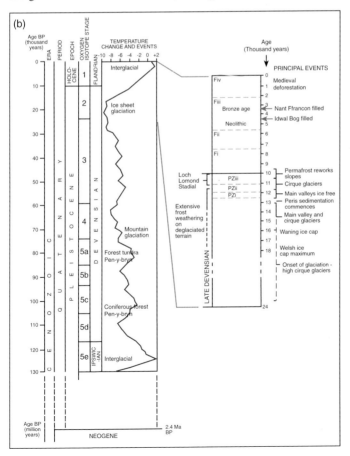

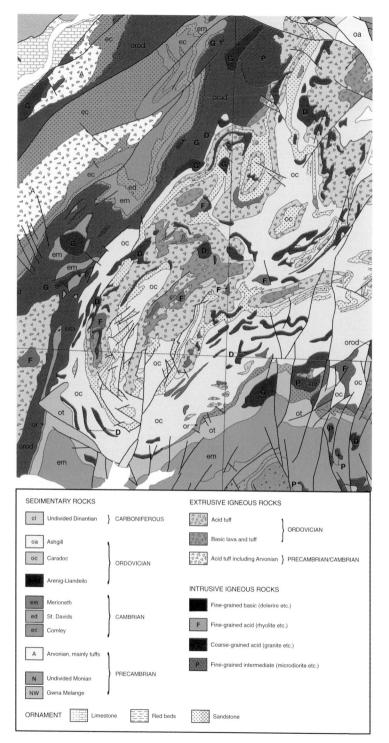

SEDIMENTARY ROCKS

| | | |
|---|---|---|
| cl | Undivided Dinantian | } CARBONIFEROUS |
| oa | Ashgill | |
| oc | Caradoc | } ORDOVICIAN |
| | Arenig-Llandeilo | |
| em | Merioneth | |
| ed | St. Davids | } CAMBRIAN |
| ec | Comley | |
| A | Arvonian, mainly tuffs | |
| N | Undivided Monian | } PRECAMBRIAN |
| NW | Gwna Melange | |

EXTRUSIVE IGNEOUS ROCKS

Acid tuff } ORDOVICIAN

Basic lava and tuff

Acid tuff including Arvonian } PRECAMBRIAN/CAMBRIAN

INTRUSIVE IGNEOUS ROCKS

Fine-grained basic (dolerire etc.)

F   Fine-grained acid (rhyolite etc.)

Coarse-grained acid (granite etc.)

P   Fine-grained intermediate (microdiorite etc.)

ORNAMENT   Limestone   Red beds   Sandstone

*Figure 2 (opposite): Bedrock geology.*

he wrote *Origin of Species*; the Reverend William Buckland, geologist and Dean of Westminster; Sir Andrew Ramsay, second Director-General of the Geological Survey; and Professor W.M. Davis, whose influence on geomorphology was so profound. It is relevant and illuminating to include their observations in this account of Snowdonia's glacial landforms, which Davis considered in 1909 to be:

'admirably developed for field study. There is nothing in the United States east of the Rocky Mountains that can be compared with North Wales in the way of vivid exhibition of ... [glacial] features.'

A modern view of Quaternary events in Snowdonia emphasises its location at a pivotal position in western Britain, flanking and

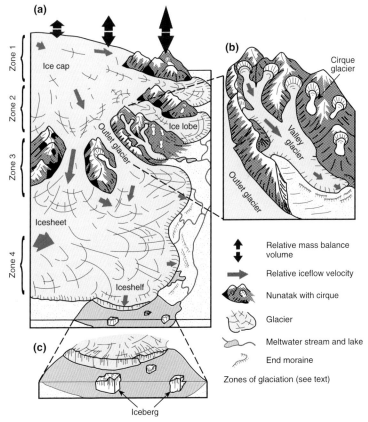

*Figure 3: Principal glacier types.*
*(a) general configuration associated with a polar ice sheet. Zones 1-4 refer to areas of Snowdonia under ice conditions identified in the text. Enlargements show (b) alpine, mountain glaciation and (c) ice shelf.*

contributing ice to the Irish Sea basin, a major discharge route for British ice sheets. Our state of knowledge and technical methods of investigation are not static. Since the first edition of this book was published in 1983, interpretation of the glacial history of Snowdonia has contended with a major **glaciomarine** theory for the Irish Sea basin, the first clear evidence of two glacial stadia (ice advance episodes) during the Devensian and major reappraisals of the timing and processes of glacial activity.

## Introduction to glaciers

Glacial landforms in Snowdonia are spectacular in scale and abundance but, since the ice which formed them has gone and the landforms are 'fossils', it is useful to review the origin, types and behaviour of glaciers (see Figure 3). Glaciers form wherever annual accumulation (snowfall, etc.) exceeds ablation (melting, etc). Outside the Polar regions, only lower temperatures and higher precipitation in mountain zones provide suitable conditions today. Above the equilibrium line, which separates the upper, accumulation zone from the lower, ablation zone, accumulating snow densifies and flows away under gravity, transferring ice to the ablation zone below.

The firnline would lie at c.2000m OD (above Ordnance Datum) today, twice the height of Snowdon, but during the Devensian cold stage it fell below the summits, initiating cirque glaciation. Enlarging cirque glaciers fed valley glaciers, a combination found in the Alps today and in Snowdonia until c.12 000 years ago and styled Alpine (temperate) glaciation. However, in colder moist Devensian phases the firnline lay below 300m, incorporating over 2000km$^2$ of North Wales into the accumulation zone. Instead of small alpine glaciers, a large Welsh ice sheet centred in the Merioneth region completely buried the upland plateaux of North Wales and flowed radially outwards. At maximum development, c.18 000 years ago, it coalesced with ice from other British centres to form the south-western portion of a British ice sheet. Polar (cold) glaciation of this sort is found today principally in Greenland, Baffin Island and the Antarctic.

Glaciologists identify many other differences between alpine and polar glaciation. Alpine regions are less cold and more humid than polar counterparts, stimulating higher rates of accumulation and ablation and a correspondingly more active mass balance or annual turnover of snow and ice. Faster turnover of ice promotes faster flow velocities, measured in tens to hundreds of metres per year. By comparison, Polar glaciers contain much colder ice, have a far longer turnover time and flow rates vary from zero (frozen to bedrock) to a few metres per year. These thermodynamic properties, the nature and rate of ice-flow and conditions at the glacier bed (including the presence or otherwise of meltwater and debris) determine the glacier's geomorphic activity and hence landforms. The following account explains the origins of Snowdonia's key glacial landforms and the glaciers which probably formed them.

# CWM IDWAL

**Photo 1: Cwm Idwal from Pen yr Ole Wen.**
*Llyn Idwal is surrounded by eight groups of moraines beneath precipitate rockwalls.*
*To centre right, major rockfalls can be seen below Twll Du.*
*Photo: Ken Addison.*

The ideal place to begin is Cwm Idwal, the most accessible site to offer a microcosm of montane glacial landforms (Figure 4). High cliffs provide a refuge for arctic-alpine flora which, together with its range of Ordovician rocks (mostly explosive volcanic products) and glacial history, led to it becoming the first Welsh National Nature Reserve. It was one of the first sites in Britain where past terrestrial glaciation was recognised, in the 1840s, when glaciation was generally ascribed to icebergs drifting over a great marine inundation (perhaps even Noah's flood!). Having missed their significance on an earlier visit, Darwin offered the first modern explanation of landforms surrounding Llyn Idwal in 1842, after seeing icebergs, terrestrial and tidewater glaciers around Tierra del Fuego:

'It is, I think, impossible for anyone who has read the descriptions of the moraines bordering the existing glaciers in the Alps, to stand on these mounds and for an instant to doubt that they are ancient moraines; ... The rocks are smoothed, mamillated and scored, all around the lake, and at

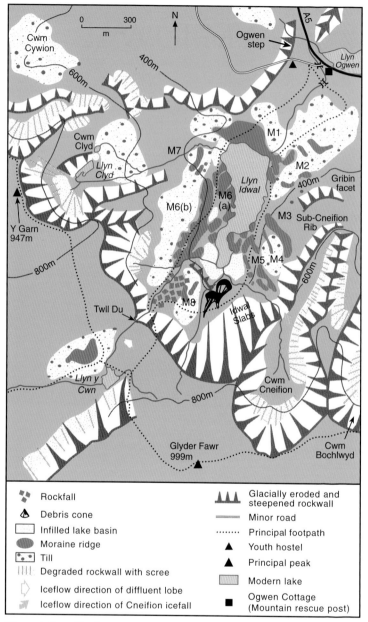

**Figure 4: Cwm Idwal.**

some depth beneath the surface ... Similar marks occur at great heights on all sides, far above the limits of the moraines just described, and were produced at the time when the ice poured in a vast stream over the rocky barrier bounding the northern end of the amphitheatre of Lake Idwell.'

Cwm Idwal possesses classic cirque features, excavated along the central syncline (downfold) of Lower Palaeozoic rocks to a maximum depth of 450m below the surrounding Glyder plateau (see Figure 4). Precipitous rockwalls surround a level floor, almost 1km long and occupied by Llyn Idwal, a shallow lake filling rapidly with sediments at its southern end. Bedrock lies at least 13m below the deepest part of the lake, rising as a natural moraine-coated dam at its northern margin. Prominent inner moraines, 35m high, are found 500m behind this outer limit. Two smaller flanking cirques overhang Cwm Idwal by 230-280m and the glacier in Cwm Cneifion in particular influenced Idwal's landforms.

## The diffluent trough

Detailed examination of the landforms indicates two recent glacial episodes but Cwm Idwal's origin cannot be fully understood without first explaining some anomalies relating to an older phase. Although the landforms of a 'textbook' cirque are present, there are also five other atypical features. The headwall is breached above Twll Du at 690m OD, 160m below its high point on Glyder Fawr. Bedrock surfaces in the breach zone still show signs of severe abrasion, despite weathering, and adjacent pockets of **till** contain **erratics** from east Snowdonia. These features suggest that extraneous ice overrode the col between Y Garn and Glyder Fawr and began to excavate the Idwal rock basin, an interpretation supported by two further anomalies: Cwm Idwal is deeper and larger than the 14 other Glyderau cirques (at 360m OD its floor lies 180-300m below most of its neighbours) and its enclosed area of 1.9km² is almost twice that of Cwm Bochlwyd, the next largest.

All this is convincing evidence in that it marks the site of a **diffluent trough** eroded under ice sheet conditions, and partial excavation gave its subsequent glaciers a 'head start' over adjacent cirques. It is not possible to date this early stage accurately, but an ice sheet surface at least 800m OD would have been required to actively override its headwall, giving a *minimum* age of the Late Devensian glacial maximum at c.18 000 years **BP**; earlier glaciation cannot be ruled out. The superficial landforms in Cwm Idwal were formed during the two more recent phases, and are younger than 18 000 years.

## Late Devensian cirque glaciation

Although excavation of Nant Ffrancon is attributed principally to the ice sheet phase, it was not finally ice-free until about 12 000 BP. During the 6000 years which thus elapsed after the glacial maximum, the ice sheet shrank and was replaced locally by independent alpine glaciers. Cwm Idwal was one of several cirques which fed a short Nant Ffrancon glacier; as Buckland observed in 1842:

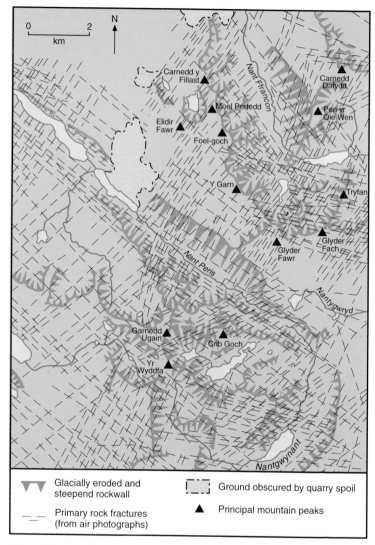

*Figure 5: Structural control of glacial erosion.*

'If at any time the mountains of Caernarvonshire were the site of lasting snows and glaciers, each of the triple series of wild amphitheatres between the summit of the Glyder and the south margin of Llynn Ogwyn must have poured forth a stream of ice to unite with those descending from Llynn Ogwyn into the valley of Nant Ffrancon.'

We can dispense with Buckland's equivocation, prompted no doubt by the contemporary debate on the nature of glaciation, and refer to the evidence. Routes into Cwm Idwal from Ogwen cottage cross an undulating, 600m-wide zone of intensely scoured bedrock surfaces, mostly buried under thin till or peat. Close examination reveals two sets of **striae** which indicate general directions of ice-flow. The older, fainter set has a west-north-west to east-south-east axis attributed to the overriding ice sheet, but the younger set cuts clearly across them on a north-north-west to south-south-east axis (Figure 5), attributed to thinner Idwal and Bochlwyd ice coalescing to form the Nant Ffrancon glacier.

Compared with its diminutive size during final glaciation, this Idwal cirque glacier was quite thick. From evidence that the Nant Ffrancon glacier was over 200m thick 2km beyond Cwm Idwal, an ice depth in excess of 250m was probable in the centre of the cirque. However, this phase was short-lived as general deglaciation proceeded, and by c.11 000 BP the entire Nant Ffrancon glacier and cirque glaciers nourishing it had probably disappeared.

## The Idwal moraines

The most recent glacial episode occurred between c.11 000-10 000 BP when a short climatic relapse re-established small cirque glaciers in Snowdonia and the Lake District, and an ice cap in western Scotland from which this re-advance event is named the **Loch Lomond Stadial**. The story of the last Idwal glacier(s) is told vividly by eight sets of moraines within the cirque, and post-glacial sediments deposited among them. It would be convenient if the outermost moraine (M1) marked the further position of the re-advancing glacier and the other seven marked progressively younger recessional stages prior to final disappearance; nature is rarely this simple. Nevertheless, the problems involved in reconstruction give useful insights into the nature of the available evidence and investigative techniques.

The **biostratigraphy** of sediments in Cwm Idwal permits the correlation of the last cirque glacier with the Loch Lomond Stadial. Sedimentation began with glacial gravels and then still-water clays indicative of ice proximity, followed by organic muds with a pollen and macrofossil assemblage typical of the post-glacial period (see Figure 6); absence of older late-glacial (Older Dryas and Allerød) sediments is ascribed to their removal by a younger cirque glacier. The sediments were found in a small, 8.25m deep peat bog among M5 moraines, which are therefore of Loch Lomond Stadial origin, and not in M1 which would have implied the simple recessional sequence. Moraines M1-M4 and M7 must be older than M5-6, otherwise the glacier which deposited the former would have removed M5-6 in its advance; but how much older, and were they deposited by the same glacier? Reasons for interpreting M1 as the late-glacial end moraine are unconvincing; the bedrock core exaggerates its size, and it is located where the classic cirque requires – at the threshold, damming a post-glacial lake. It might be referred instead to the shrinking Late Devensian glacier, located where the threshold increased frictional drag in basal ice, inducing deposition. This view is strengthened where M1 merges with diffuse, fluted moraines (M2) below the Gribin facet marking no clear glacial limit. Moraines M3-4 are not as

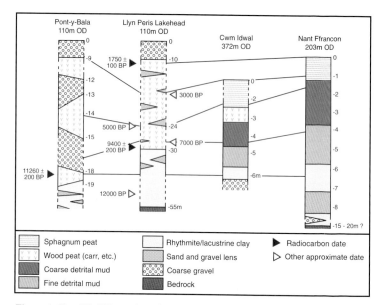

*Figure 6: Simplified biostratigraphy of lake sediments.*
*Lines between columns link units of similar age. Broken lines show telescoping of sequence in same unit for convenience; depths in metres below OD.*

immediately obvious as the cirque floor moraines. With upper elements of M5 they rise diagonally across the east wall from the lake shore. M3 rises over 100m above the lake and although bedrock is never far from its surface, it is a substantial lateral moraine. M4 is much thinner, identifiable mostly where streams dissect its surface, and the hummocky moraines (M5) which run into the lake begin as thick till 150m higher.

The significance of the cirque overhanging the east wall of Cwm Idwal now becomes obvious, for these three lateral moraines (with no west wall counterparts) are aligned with the exit of Cwm Cneifion and contain distinctive erratics. The Cneifion glacier, accelerating as an **icefall** over the cliffs below, substantially reinforced the mass, impetus and volume of debris of the Idwal glacier and it is significant that the largest moraines (M6) lie directly opposite Cneifion on the west lake shore. They can be divided into two sub-sets: a lower cluster of hummocky lakeside mounds (M6(a)) separated by eroded peat bog, and an arcuate ridge 600m long and up to 35m high (M6(b)). The former have been interpreted as a lateral moraine but the latter as a **protalus rampart** formed below a snow patch on the west wall. This attaches more significance to a transient snow patch than to a powerful cirque glacier, deflected westwards across Cwm Idwal by the icefall. However, erratic breccias and tuffs from the east wall/Cneifion region and basalt from Twll Du appear in this ridge, suggesting that M6(b) was bulldozed by a composite Idwal-Cneifion glacier from the base of the icefall (Photo 2). It represents an earlier terminus of thicker ice, moulded against the west wall, than M5,

*Photo 2: The '3000ft' plateau of Glyder Fach and Glyder Fawr dramatically overhangs Nant Ffrancon.*
*The plateau is probably a surviving remnant of a land surface elevated during the mid-Tertiary, before Quaternary glaciation. Its north face was dissected by glaciers in (left to right) Cwm Bochlywyd, Cneifion and Idwal. Photo: Ken Addison.*

M6(a) and M8 which once formed a continuous feature, breached as the lake filled post-glacially. The less impressive 'end' moraines M1-M2 and M7 are too subdued and distant to be regarded as contemporaries and they may substantially pre-date the Loch Lomond Stadial.

## Idwal Slabs and Twll Du

An account of Cwm Idwal would be incomplete without describing erosional landforms and their influence on post-glacial processes, although they do not afford direct means of dating and reconstructing events. Rotational flow (described on page 37) in the Idwal glacier, at the Cneifion icefall and in the earlier diffluent trough glacier was responsible for excavating the Idwal rock basin and the reverse slope of its threshold. The basin was enlarged primarily by the destabilisation and failure of rockwalls by glacier undercutting and by abrasion and quarrying of the floor; evidence of these processes is abundant. Bedrock floor surfaces were heavily abraded by debris-impregnated basal ice but more impressive signs of glacial erosion are found in the extensive rockwalls of the Idwal Slabs and flanking Twll Du where ice exploited the geological structure. Parallel bedding-planes in steeply dipping (inclined) Lower Rhyolitic Tuffs form the Idwal Slabs, with slope angle and dip identical at 55-60°. Around Twll Du, at right angles to the Slabs, bedding-planes only appear as a series of narrow ledges curving upwards away from the ravine eroded along the syncline axis. Small amounts of glacial erosion near the base of the developing cliffs destabilised the rock along these fracture planes, causing considerably larger rock volumes to fail repeatedly onto the glacier surface. Minor cliffs aligned across the Cwm not far above the lakehead, mark the backwall foot, a stepped zone where near-horizontal fractures in the floor took over erosional control from vertical fractures in the headwall as predominantly downward ice vectors in the accumulation zone gave way to horizontal (and even upward) vectors in the ablation zone.

Although the Slabs rise 400m above the cirque floor, absence of large rock debris at their base indicates a glacier's ability to transport eroded rock and demonstrates that Cwm Idwal was mostly excavated before the Loch Lomond Stadial. Moraines account for only a small fraction of the volume of rock removed from the Idwal and Cneifion basins. Rockwalls have continued to fail in the **Holocene** due to prior steepening beyond equilibrium-angle during glacial erosion. Only 150m of cliffs survive around Twll Du and the enormous rockfall and other blocks littering its lower slopes must have fallen after the ice had gone. Most lower slopes are mantled by screes, and active processes today are associated with frost weathering at high elevation, rapid debris transport by steep torrents and free fall down gullies. Destabilisation near footpaths also accelerates erosion, demonstrating landscape sensitivity to visitor pressures. Many debris fans are superimposed on the glacial landforms, the largest found between Twll Du and the Idwal Slabs (see Figure 4). Fine debris washed from them is responsible for rapid sedimentation near the lakehead, where colonisation first by aquatic and then terrestrial plants completes the veil being drawn gradually over the Ice Age.

### Access

Two routes lead into Cwm Idwal from the car park near the Ogwen Snack Bar and Mountain Rescue Post at Ogwen cottage (SH 650604). The eastern route is better marked; the western route provides direct access to the western moraines, giving a view down Nant Ffrancon from the abraded rock step en route. All landforms are visible from the highest moraine (30 minutes); the lake shore can be reached in 20 minutes, but the most rewarding excursion encircles the lake via the lakehead or the base of Twll Du (2½ hours). Proper clothing and footwear are essential, and visitors are reminded that Cwm Idwal is a National Nature Reserve.

# THE NORTHERN GLYDERAU CIRQUES

Cirque glaciers are the smallest active ice bodies, sensitive to short-term climate change by virtue of their mass balance characteristics. Accumulation and ablation rates are high in proportion to mass, with annual turnover of perhaps 1-3% compared with less than 0.1% for a modest sub-polar ice cap; enlargement into a valley glacier, or wasting and decay, may occur within decades. Mass balance in turn drives ice-flow regime and hence geomorphic activity, and cirque glaciers provide a simple model of general glacier behaviour. During a mass budget year, winter gain from snowfall, wind-drift and avalanching is offset by summer melt of snow and ice. The equilibrium line separates higher areas of net accumulation from lower areas of net ablation and, on modern cirque glaciers, appears roughly three-fifths of the vertical distance between the glacier terminus and headwall crest. Consequential steepening of the glacier surface increases internal stress in the readily-deformable ice, inducing rotational ice-flow through a combination of internal deformation and basal sliding mechanisms (see Figure 7). The former describes forward motion accomplished by the plastic realignment of ice crystals under the glacier's own weight whilst, in the latter, the

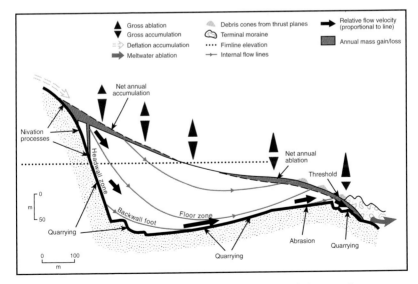

*Figure 7: Cirque glacier mass balance, flow and processes. Relative annual amounts of accumulation and ablation are shown. Vertical scale is twice horizontal.*

***Photo 3: Northern Glyderau cirques on the west flank of Nant Ffrancon***
*Steep rockwalls in Cwm Coch (left cente) excavated in microgranite contrast with the subdued cirques Cwm Bual and Cwm Perfedd (right) in slate. The flat, marshy floor of Nant Ffrancon is punctuated by debris fans. Photo: Ken Addison*

glacier slides bodily over a wet base. In steady state (annual gross accumulation = annual net ablation) a cirque glacier will transfer just enough ice into the ablation zone to match the loss and, in this way, ice-flow volume and velocity respond to mass balance. Velocity is at its maximum at depth under the equilibrium line and drives glacial erosion.

Not only are cirque glaciers sensitive to local climatic controls but bedrock strength influences their erosive power more than for larger glaciers. These controls on cirque form, location and shape are well illustrated in the Glyderau cirques (Photo 3 and Figure 8 on page 28) which are strikingly uniform in aspect and elevation – parameters to which glaciologists attach great significance.

## Climatic control

A spect assumes that solar radiation contributes least to ablation on slopes facing between north-west and north-east, and snow deflation (wind-drift) from exposed, windward slopes substantially augments accumulation on sheltered lee slopes. Some 70% of Snowdonia's cirques face between north and east. All 15 Glyderau cirques possess a north-north-east aspect, and the orientation (glacier axis alignment inferred from moraines and headway) of the northern Glyderau group is concentrated between 040°- 073°. None of the ten cirques in this group departs more than 27° from the mean orientation of 046° and all lie south and west of Nant Ffrancon; they are deep in shade long before the east side and, despite its elevation, Pen yr Ole

Wen (978m OD) supported no more than a permanent snowbed there on west-facing cliffs.

Elevation reflects the equilibrium line altitude (ELA) during cirque formation and the diminutive size of cirque glaciers compared with other glaciers should facilitate reconstruction of the ELA. However, error or uncertainty may arise depending on the cirque parameters selected, how the former glacier terminus position is marked and whether the cirque was occupied more than once. Efforts to reconstruct the Loch Lomond Stadial ELA, in particular, depend mostly on subjective assumptions about the 'freshness' of moraines (the more reliable constraint of a radiocarbon date is a rare option) and cannot evaluate the climatic advantage attached to a pre-existing, sheltered cirque basin during a subsequent stadial. Bearing in mind that all reconstructions are approximations, Table 1 shows data for ten cirques and indicates two ELAs. Cwm Idwal and six cirques north of Cwm Clyd lie within 43m of a lower ELA at 653m OD, and Clyd, Cneifion and Bochlwyd are within 17m of a mean ELA at 793m OD. One reason is not hard to find: the Glyderau plateau (Photo 4) remnants of Y Garn, Glyder Fawr and Glyder Fach (947m, 999m and 994m OD respectively) provided substantial protection and deflation sources for accumulation zones in their lee and the three highest cirque glaciers formed on their north-east faces. By comparison, only 20-30m of the summits of Carnedd y Filiast, Moel Perfedd and Foel-goch lie above 793m, offering insignificant source and protection zones, and the snowline had to fall further before their respective cirque glaciers formed.

Protection from insolation was thus a crucial climatic factor in the orientation of Glyderau cirque glaciers, and explains their absence from the east side of Nant Ffrancon. The extent of wind-drifted accumulation is less certain, however. Parallels between an estimated rise in the ELA from south-west to north-east in Snowdonia and an eastward decline in modern precipitation might suggest that Devensian winds were, like today, predominantly south-westerly (augmenting accumulation on north-east facing slopes). We should not assume so much from cirque orientation. The concentration of

Table 1: Northern Glyder cirque data

| Cirque | Firnline altitude (m) | Orientation (°) | Manley ratio | Floor lithology | Wall lithology |
|--------|------------------------|------------------|--------------|-----------------|----------------|
| Ceunant | 630[1] | 040 | 2.5 | slate | grit |
| Grainanog | 610[1] | 042 | 2.3 | grit | grit/granite |
| Perfedd | 670[1] | 051 | 2.0 | slate | granite/slate |
| Bual | 670[1] | 059 | 2.3 | slate | slate |
| Coch | 670[1] | 060 | 1.8 | slate | granite |
| Cywion | 690[1] | 048 | 2.8 | slate | granite/dol/tuff |
| Clyd | 810[2] | 073 | 2.1 | sandstone/tuff | sandstone/tuff |
| Idwal | 630[1] | 038 | 3.6 | tuff | tuff/basalt |
| Cneifion | 790[2] | 020 | 2.6 | slate | basalt/tuff |
| Bochlwyd | 780[2] | 025 | 3.6 | slate | rhy/CB |

Mean value: firnline 1. 652.8m; 2. 793.0m; orientation 045.6°

*Photo 4: Perfect structural control seen in the north wall of Cwm Graianog, which slopes down the tilted bedding planes of Cambrian grits. The Graianog glacier undercut this rockwall, triggering planar slides. Photo: Ken Addison.*

north-east facing cirques in the Glyderau is not so marked on Snowdon and elsewhere. Scottish studies link late-glacial snowfall with south-south-east winds, and westerly atmospheric circulation was replaced during glacial maxima by a polar anticyclone over the Scandinavian Ice Sheet. Two further factors seriously challenge the totality of climatic control on cirque formation – undeniable geological control and the significance of the Nant Ffrancon trough.

## Geological control

There are few clearer illustrations of geological controls on glacier erosion than the association of cirque orientation with lithological outcrops and structure, exposed superbly in the Cambrian and Ordovician rock sequence on the west flank of Nant Ffrancon. Rock strength is determined by lithology (intrinsic properties such as mineralogy, crystalline or cement bonding, particle size, void ratio, etc.) and also by structure, ie. the geometric arrangement of discontinuities (joints, faults, fractures, cleavage) inherited principally from earth movements. The rocks are downfolded south-eastwards towards the central Snowdon Syncline axis running through Cwm Idwal; each lithological unit outcrops along a north-east to south-west strike (direction) (Figure 2) which parallels the primary, Caledonian tectonic structural pattern (Figure 5). The Glyderau plateau reflects broad lithologic differences, with the highest ground associated with the greatest concentration of igneous rocks (tuffs, basalts, etc.). North of Foel-goch weaker mudstones form the lowest ground between summits located on intermediate-strength microgranites and Cambrian Grits and rise 100m above the cols. This pattern is accentuated in the cirques, since glaciers oversteepen mountain slopes and only mechanically strong rocks can support substantial rockwalls. Seven cirque floors are excavated in mudstone and associated weak, silty sandstones, whereas six have sidewalls of resistant igneous rock. Perfedd and Bual, the two least impressive cirques, were excavated along the widest mudstone outcrop with degraded headwalls scarcely 50m high. Their subdued mutual divide contrasts with the north wall of Perfedd, which rises steeply 170m above the granodiorite contact, and Graianog, with rockwalls consistently 200m high in granodiorite and massive Carnedd y Filiast grit. Where this gives way to Marchlyn mudstone, Ceunant's head-and north-wall are less than 50m in height.

South of Foel-goch, Ordovician marine sediments become interbedded increasingly with eruptive and intrusive igneous rocks. Foel-goch microgranite forms the south wall of Coch and its metamorphic impact stiffens the north wall. Cywion's widest basin is in mudstones and sandstones but dolerite forms a vertical cliff below the south wall, and similar alternations between resistant tuffs and weak mudstones make Clyd a more complex, irregular cirque. Idwal again provides an exception to the general pattern; although located in the widest outcrop of igneous rocks (tuffs and basalts), disregard of these stronger strata echoes earlier origins under thicker, overriding ice and its glaciers also exploited the syncline axis. Mudstones form the floor of Cneifion and most of Bochlwyd, with rockwalls in tuffs; the imposing 230m east wall of Bochlwyd is cut in Capel Curig Volcanic Formation tuffs reinforced by intrusive rhyolite.

Preference for weaker strata demonstrates lithological control on cirque sites, excavated along the strike, but structural influences were even more decisive. Discontinuities occur in orthogonal fracture sets, consisting usually of two near-vertical and one near-horizontal set, rendering rockmass mechanically defective in directions reflecting the fracture geometry. This is essential for glacial erosion since ice, with a shear strength of c.0.1MN m$^{-2}$ (mega newtons per square metre), cannot compete with otherwise-intact rock; granite, for example, has a shear strength of up to 140MN m$^{-2}$. Failure is determined by rock rather than ice properties and quarrying (as distinct from abrasion, which is a superficial and self-limiting process) operates by removal of rockmass along the fractures. The effective stress applied by a moving glacier has much less work to do in the presence of such large-scale loss of rockmass cohesion and is also assisted greatly by basal meltwater. Trapped between ice and rock and usually under high pressure, this adds its own shear stress while reducing bedrock friction strength. Rockwalls above the glacier surface do not escape; oversteepened by sub-glacial erosion, the same fractures provide release planes for sliding and toppling rockwall failures onto the glacier.

Evidence of geological control is widespread; locally, most

rockwalls are seen to consist of three sets of angular faces with one dominant. Fine examples occur in the north wall of Graianog, controlled by south-east-facing discontinuities clearly visible from the A5, and the Idwal Slabs, where strike-discontinuities (facing north-west) determine the direction and angle of rockwalls (Photo 4). Cleavage planes mimic the primary fracture axis in most rocks, especially mudstones (slates) and other fine-grained sedimentary and igneous rocks. Their millimetre spacing is too close to aid glacial erosion but is susceptible to frost action, assisting subsequent scree formation and rockwall degradation.

Regionally, cirque orientation conforms to the primary north-east to south-west Caledonian structures with striking fidelity; floors are excavated along the primary axis while headwalls show rock failure along the secondary (north-west to south-east) axis. The east-north-east alignment of northern cirques gives way to a north-north-east orientation in Idwal, Cneifion and Bochlwyd in perfect harmony with a swing in the primary axis. Strike-oriented cirques develop distinctive shapes; only Idwal and Bochlwyd possess true bedrock basins which now impound lakes. There is no true basin in Clyd, its lakes being impounded by strike ridge and peat infill, and lakelets in Cywion nestle in morainic ground. In seven cirques (all except Idwal, Bochlwyd and Clyd) the floor falls continuously away from the headway and classic long profiles are absent. This is widely considered to indicate immature development, measured by the 'Manley ratio' of plan length to vertical extent, with mature cirques exceeding 3:1. Only Idwal and Bochlwyd fall into this class (Table 1) and in plan area they are also the largest. Nevertheless, evident geological control challenges the traditional supremacy of climate on cirque development and morphology.

## Moraines

Few of the northern Glyderau cirques have substantial moraines, and the most impressive are in Idwal. Usually, hummocky morainic material is spread over cirque floors, with more substantial ridges in Bochlwyd; and in Graianog block size reflects very large rockfalls onto the glacier as it destabilised Carnedd y Filiast grit. In Coch, a narrow tongue of ice extended far enough to overhang the ledge above Nant Ffrancon. Two large moraines, eroded by modern streams, mark former terminal positions. The outer moraine approaches the valley floor but may exaggerate the glacier's true depth, for the snout would have accelerated over the ledge and thinned appreciably. It was only 50m wide just behind the terminus and no more than 15-20m thick. The inner moraine 100m higher may be a more reliable measure of the Loch Lomond Stadial glacier. Glyderau moraines highlight the pros and cons of trying to date events solely from landforms; they are assigned to Loch Lomond Stadial glaciers, or older cirque advance or retreat episodes, on the basis of their relative positions, apparent 'freshness' of shape (including high slope angles) and size. The presence of dateable organo-sediments ponded by moraines obviates reliance on these imprecise and haphazard techniques.

## Access

The cirques are visible and accessible from Nant Ffrancon. Because they are so high, direct access should only be undertaken by properly equipped and experienced walkers. Individually, Coch and especially Graianog are the most interesting, reached from the minor road on the west valley side. Coch is reached across the moraine 300m south of Pentre Farm (SH 639615) (2 hours), and Graianog via a path alongside the wall rising into its north-east corner from Tai-newyddion (SH 630635); moraines, and slab and wedge failure in the north wall, can be studied from close quarters (3 hours) and a scramble up the microgranite crest of the south wall leads to the summit plateau (4 hours). One of the most rewarding mountain walks in Britain runs the full length of the North Glyderau plateau, commanding views of the cirques, Nant Ffrancon, Llanberis Pass and Snowdon. Access is from the minor road 200m north of Tai-newyddion; climb onto the Ffronllwydd ridge or via Cwm Ceunant (2 hours), then 4km along the summit plateau to Y Garn (SH 631596) (4 hours) and descend via the path to the south side of Twll Du, past Llyn Idwal to Ogwen cottage (SH 650604) (6-7 hours). The reverse route is more arduous! For proper study, allow a full day when the cloud base is above 1000m.

# NANT FFRANCON

**Photo 5: The rockwall flanking Nant Ffrancon to the east, below Pen yr Ole Wen.**
*The absence of cirques contrasts with the Glyderau flank in Photo 3. The rockwall is marked instead by rock pinnacles, chutes and screes indicative of severe frost weathering as the Nant Ffrancon glacier shrank and finally disappeared. Modern debris flow tracks score the scree surface. Photo: Ken Addison.*

'I do assure the traveller who delights in wild nature, that a visit to ... Nant Ffrancon from Bangor will not be repented. The waters of five lakes dart down the precipice of the middle of the Benglog and form the torrent of the Ogwen. The bottom is surrounded with mountains of stupendous height, mostly precipitous; the tops of many edged with pointed rocks.'

Thomas Pennant's description of Nant Ffrancon in 1773 reflects the grandeur of one of Britain's best known highland valleys and summarises its essential landscape ingredients (see Figure 8). There are four sharply-discordant elements; first, the valley cuts abruptly c.700m into the otherwise continuous Glyderau-Carneddau summit plateau (see Photo 2). This is striking when seen from the north, but best appreciated from the plateau itself. Next, precipitous valley sides give way to a notably level valley floor at 200m OD as they pass beneath its sediments. Third, the absence of cirques on the east wall

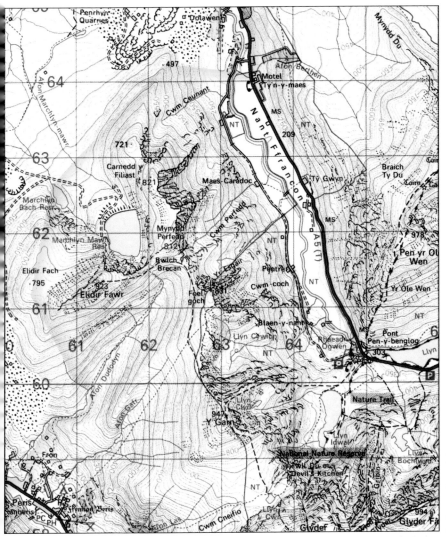

(Photo 5) contrasts with seven etched along the west wall north of Cwm Idwal. Finally, the floor drops sharply 170m below the riegel of Pen-y-benglog and by 105m at its southern end, creating the waterfalls of Rhaeadr Ogwen. While this strictly marks the head of Nant Ffrancon, the 5km-long trough is part of a longer through valley which cuts across the geologic and topographic axis of Snowdonia.

Nant Ffrancon shows clear evidence of the effects of alpine and ice-sheet glaciation, although its origins are not free from controversy. Mid-nineteenth century views generally invoked a tidewater glacier, nourished from cirques north of Bochlwyd, whose moraines were washed out as ice retreated and the lower valley became a tidal inlet. Later, despite Davis' conviction in 1909 of major erosion by thick ice,

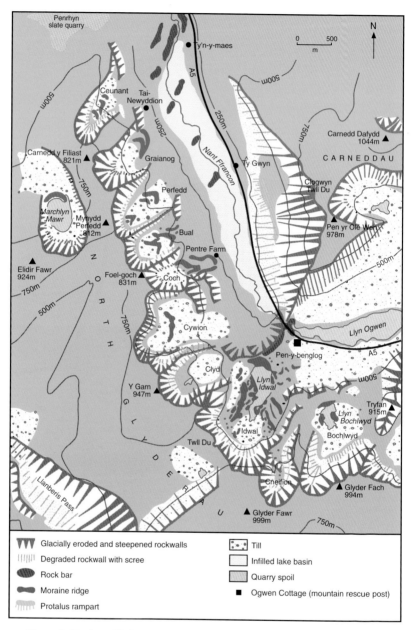

*Figure 8: Northern Glyderau cirques and Nant Ffrancon.*

many followers attributed only minor overdeepening of deep, pre-glacial canyons to local glaciers. As recently as 1976, Dury preferred a pre-glacial watershed near Foel-goch (although Glyder summits to the east are over 170m higher), with ice as far west as Cywion flowing

***Photo 6: The glacial breach at Ogwen Cottage, seen from Y Garn.***
*Llyn Ogwen (centre), Llyn Idwal (right) and the central Glyderau cirques attest to intense glacial erosion. Photo: Ken Addison.*

*eastward* before breaching the watershed and excavating Nant Ffrancon (Photo 6). The valley's origin cannot be explained, however, solely by local glaciation.

It has long been known that Welsh ice entered England; in 1898 erratics in the Wolverhampton-Birmingham area were traced to the Arenig region 30km east of Snowdon, and Welsh tills form the youngest units in thick glacigenic sediments around Shrewsbury. The Late Devensian ice centre was located in the Migneint-Arenig region of Merioneth (see Figure 14 on page 51), not near Snowdon, and was a considerable accumulation up to 1000m thick. It is inconceivable that radial outflow capable of taking ice 75-140km east into north-east Wales and the West Midlands was ineffective to the west. Although Snowdon presented a barrier to north-west outflow, it was overridden to c.900m OD and **transfluent troughs** developed where ice escaped across cols. Outlet glaciers, draining the ice sheet through these troughs, concentrated and accelerated ice in these zones, with dramatic increases in erosive power, and swept Migneint-Arenig erratics into the coastal lowlands. Nant Ffrancon and the Llanberis Pass are the largest of several outlet troughs formed in this way, in an arc on the north-west flank of the Ice Sheet.

The depth and impact of overriding ice is difficult to estimate because Nant Ffrancon is a compound feature; there is evidence of a lesser trough within the main valley and the cirques exuded glaciers long after the outlet glacier disappeared. There is no doubt, however, that a major ice-stream, and not a local glacier, breached the Glyderau-Carneddau plateau. Principal features associated with major transfluent breaches beneath former ice sheets in Scotland, Scandinavia and North America are present. The watershed has been profoundly remodelled. A rock basin, now occupied by Llyn Ogwen, lies in the former watershed zone; bedrock surfaces throughout this region are intensely scoured, with striations at considerable heights and oversteepened slopes cut through the summit plateau, especially on Pen yr Ole Wen.

Breaching focused at the riegel above Nant Ffrancon. The Snowdon-Glyder Fawr-Carneddau mountain crest follows the Ordovician synclinal axis and, glacial breaches apart, modern drainage follows this ancient divide. However, the modern watershed is now an insignificant bedrock ridge only 315m OD at Pont Rhyd-goch, 2.9km east of Rhaeadr Ogwen, and for at least 2.5km the floor is a shallow rock basin up to 12m deep. Llyn Ogwen occupies the western 1.6km of this basin, infilled from Gwern Gof Uchaf to the lakehead. Most bedrock surfaces around Llyn Ogwen and south towards Idwal and Bochlwyd testify to intense glacial scour and many display classic **roche moutonnée** forms. Similar, though more weathered, marks are found up to 660m above lake level on Pen yr Ole Wen, where the absence of cirques makes assessment of ice thickness easier; seen from the Glyderau, the degree to which Pen yr Ole Wen has been torn through is stunning.

To the west, several spurs separating Glyder cirques were truncated at two distinct levels. The intermittent lower level falls from c.500m OD on Cwm Clyd's north ridge and above Pentre Farm, to 480m at yr Galen and 400m below Graianog, and may mark the limit of the Nant Ffrancon alpine glacier succeeding the ice sheet. Spurs and associated cliffs are more strongly abraded north of each cirque. We find that the higher truncations are even more intermittent, but are also deflected and decline northwards from about 900m OD on Y Garn's north ridge, 750m on Y Llymllwyd and 680m on Graianog's south ridge, continuing as heavily abraded rock on the broad divide between Graianog and Ceunant.

The absence of cirques from the east wall of Nant Ffrancon precludes a matching pattern below Pen yr Ole Wen and emphasises the tenuous nature of cirque glaciation. Only higher insolation on its south-west face permitted a permanent snowpatch to develop there and a huge protalus rampart 400m long marks its position. Derived from encircling cliffs at Clogwyn Braich Ty Du by **nivation** processes debris slid over, or washed under, the snowbed to its toe, continuing downslope to form a rubble apron 100m high. The snowbed extended for about 400m above the rampart crest and was generally less than 20m thick. This, together with a surface slope of 35°, rules out the possibility that it developed into a glacier.

Despite this valley cross-sectional asymmetry, the west wall truncations suggest that a major, north-west-moving ice stream with a surface gradient of 7-10° breached the summit plateau (see Figure 9).

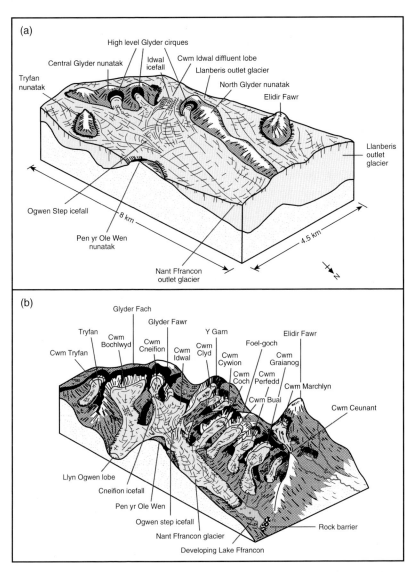

*Figure 9: Reconstruction of glacial conditions in Nant Ffrancon and North Glyderau, showing the probable appearance of glaciers at (a) about 18 000 BP the Welsh ice sheet maximum, and (b) about 13 000 BP after its decay and replacement with local valley and cirque glaciers.*

Whether the cirque glaciers were tributaries to this outlet glacier or (as is more likely) the later Nant Ffrancon valley glacier, normal gravity outflow was prevented and they were deflected northwards by main valley ice. The lion's share of excavation is attributed to Welsh ice sheet activity and a lesser amount to earlier and subsequent Nant Ffrancon glaciers. The riegel at Rhaeadr Ogwen lies 660m below the excavation limit on Pen yr Ole Wen and is in turn 105m above the valley floor, which acts as a major sediment trap for modern streams. Borehole evidence suggests that the bedrock floor is perhaps another 10m below the base of the riegel, giving at most 775m of glacial excavation at the south end of Nant Ffrancon. How much of this occurred in the Devensian cold stage and how much in earlier glaciations is beyond current analysis.

# The former Nant Ffrancon lake

For most of its life since glaciation, Nant Ffrancon held a lake up to 3km long infilled progressively by sediments swept from the surrounding slopes and decanted through its waters. The sediments occupy a rock basin barred originally to the north by a 12m high roche moutonnée, and a small riegel near Maes-Caradoc (SH 635626) may have divided the shrinking lake in two. The southern basin was probably filled first since the valley narrows upstream and attracts greater sediment supply from higher surrounding mountains. A borehole core from the northern basin (see Figure 6) indicates that sedimentation began with basal gravels and clays immediately after the valley glacier withdrew, leaving a rock basin up to 40m deep behind the roche moutonnée.

The pollen assemblage in overlying organic muds is typical of late-glacial climatic amelioration, with very low levels of tree pollen including the tundra dwarf birch *Betula nana*. Arboreal pollen increases upwards prior to a sharp decline immediately below c.1m of soliflucted minerogenic clays correlated with the Loch Lomond Stadial. A resumption of tundra species gives way rapidly, first to willow and pine and later oak and elm, correlating with the post-glacial development of woodland in Nant Ffrancon. Reed-swamp developed around the shrinking lake margins and infixing ended with the formation of raised sphagnum peat bogs. Despite drainage, marshy areas still survive, and debris fans from streams and rockfalls continue to spread across the lake sediments. The largest fans mark the sites of farms and home pasture at Maes-Caradoc and Pentre Farm.

### Access

Access is obtained from the A5 on the east valley side, or minor road on the west side between Ogwen cottage (SH 650604) and Ty'n-y-maes (SH 634643) – both on the A5. The west route also affords access to the Glyderau cirques and their panorama of Nant Ffrancon and Pen-y-benglog (SH 646602). Within the valley, a circular walk northwards along the A5 from Ogwen Cottage gives good views across to the cirques, returning southwards with the best views of the Ogwen riegel and enclosing plateaux. The full route (10km) takes approximately 2 hours, but can be shortened to 5.6km (1¼ hr) by crossing the valley floor via the footpath and footbridge between Tŷ Gwyn (SH 641627) and Maes-Caradoc (SH 635626).

# SNOWDON

Snowdon possesses a unique grandeur. As well as being the highest mountain in England and Wales (1085m OD) and giving its name to the range, the summit, Yr Wyddfa, crowns five major ridges radiating over a 80km² base. Three glacial troughs with floors up to 1000m lower isolate it from adjacent mountains (see Figure 10). The combined bulk of Snowdon and its glaciers prevented it from being overrun by the ice sheet. Although not at the dispersal point of Welsh ices it was a bastion of alpine, mountain glaciation in North Wales which altered its rounded pre-glacial form so profoundly that even W.M. Davis, a 'father' of geomorphology and proponent of cycles of continental denudation, wrote in 1909:

> '... this full-bodied mass was transformed during the Glacial Period, and chiefly by glacial excavation of valley-head cwms and by the glacial widening and deepening of the valleys themselves, into a sharp central peak, which gives forth acutely serrated ridges between wide amphitheatres.'

The alpine glaciation which virtually destroyed the pre-glacial summit surface is the subject of this section. In classic terms, Yr Wyddfa and its satellite Garnedd Ugain are residual pyramidal peaks or horns, formed by progressive headway retreat of encircling glaciers enlarging their cirques. Where an individual cirque glacier cut back into the summit surface, as at Y Lliwedd, an asymmetric ridge was formed. Where two or more cirques eroded back-to-back their divide became a precipitous **arête** (Crib Goch and Bwlch Main), and continued erosion destroyed the divide (Bwlch Coch and Bwlch Ciliau). Ten cirques encroach on the summits from all sides, with less evident climatic and geological control than in the Glyderau.

Aspect, orientation and elevation of Snowdon cirques are so variable that group mean values are probably meaningless and more than one generation can be identified (Table 2 on page 37). Seven cirques have an easterly aspect and, Glaslyn and Llydaw excepted (Photo 7 on page 36), are quite small. The three remaining cirques are large; Tregalan faces south-east and Clogwyn and Du'r Arddu (Photo 8 on page 36) north-west. This asymmetry ensured more extensive excavation on Snowdon's east and north flanks and that the surviving summit plateau faces west. Furthermore, whereas five of the seven eastern cirques (Llydaw, Glaslyn, Upper Glaslyn, Glas and Uchaf) cut through to the summit surface, Du'r Arddu does not, and Clogwyn and Tregalan do so only where they meet at Bwlch Main. The mean

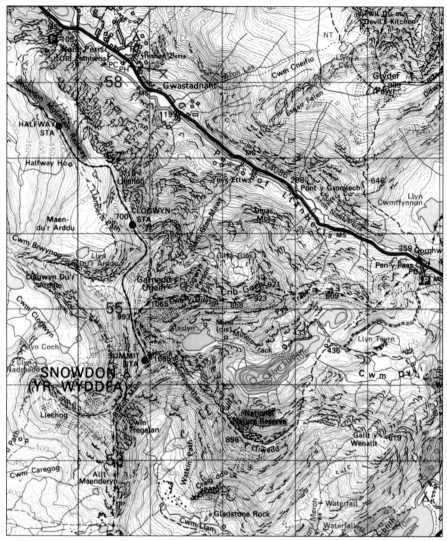

ELA of the six largest cirques was 688m OD (variation less than 58m), and only Llydaw has an east aspect. By comparison, the four smallest cirques, within 55m of their mean firnline of 835m, have a north-easterly aspect and are orientated within 40° of a mean of 050°. Glas Bach, Glas Mawr, Glas and Uchaf were strongly influenced by the excavation of the Llanberis Pass.

Structural control is still evident but the effect of lithological variations is generally slight. All cirques coincide with one of three primary fracture alignments; north-north-east to south-south-west (primary Caledonian) fractures control four cirques above the Llanberis Pass, and west-north-west to east-north-east fractures control the two western cirques and Tregalan. The Snowdon

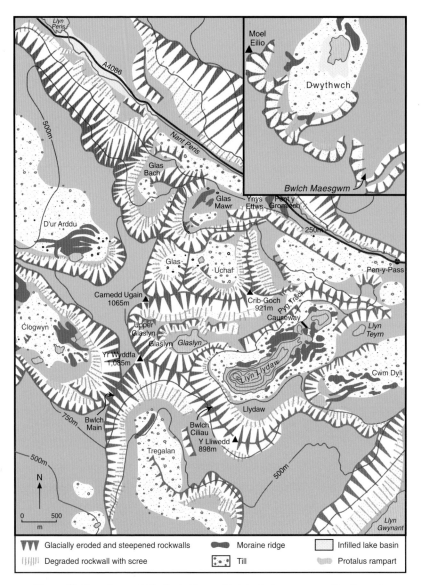

*Figure 10: Snowdon and Llanberis Pass,* with lake bed contours at 10m intervals
shown in Llyn Lydaw. Inset: Cwm Dwythwch and Moel Eilio, which lie 5km north-west
of Cwm Clogwyn.

Horseshoe (three cirques) was excavated along east-north-east to
west-south-west variants of the primary fractures. There is no
detectable pattern of lithological control, however, since the massif is
composed primarily of mechanically strong pyroclasts (welded ash,
etc., from explosive volcanic eruptions) at the core of the Snowdon
Syncline; Lower Rhyolitic Tuffs occupy lower ground and Bedded
Pyroclasts the remnant summits. Glacial erosion had few zones of less

*Photo 7: Intense glacial erosion excavated a cirque staircase on Snowdon, from Cwm Glaslyn (foreground) to Cwm Llydaw (left) and beyond. Photo: Ken Addison.*

*Photo 8: Cwm D'ur Arddu makes a dramatic, local impression on the otherwise more rounded north-west flank of Snowdon (cp. Photo 7). Photo: Ken Addison.*

competent strata to exploit and lithological differences, such as a dolerite intrusion forming the threshold to Clogwyn and intrusive rhyolite resisting headway destruction at Crib Goch, merely ornament the cirques. Prominent cliffs and the fresh appearance of much ice-abraded rock are due to greater mechanical strength and resistance to post-glacial weathering of the igneous rocks.

Table 2: Snowdon cirque data

| Cirque | Firnline altitude (m) | Orientation (°) | Manley ratio | Floor lithology | Wall lithology |
|--------|----------------------|-----------------|--------------|-----------------|----------------|
| Glas Bach | 630[1] | 033 | 2.1 | tuff | BP |
| Glas Mawr | 720[1] | 037 | 2.6 | tuff | tuff |
| Glas | 840[2] | 040 | 2.6 | BP/tuff | BP/tuff |
| Uchaf | 790[2] | 010 | 2.8 | BP | BP/rhy |
| Glaslyn | 820[2] | 060 | 2.7 | tuff | tuff/BP |
| Upper Glaslyn | 890[2] | 090 | 2.4 | BP | BP |
| Llydaw | 640[1] | 030 | 3.8 | tuff | tuff |
| Tregalan | 690[1] | 140[3] | 2.8 | slate | tuff |
| Clogwyn | 740[1] | 320[3] | 3.0 | tuff/dol | tuff/BP |
| Du'r Arddu | 710[1] | 340[3] | 3.1 | tuff | tuff/dol |

Mean value: firnline 1. 688m; 2. 835.0m; orientation 042.8° (3. excluded).

# The Snowdon Horseshoe

The compound eastern basin of Snowdon is the massif's largest glacial excavation, encircled horseshoe-like by the Y Lliwedd and Crib Goch (Photo 9) arêtes; its three cirques contain two of Snowdonia's largest and deepest cirque lakes. Sufficient elevation and prolonged mountain glaciation permitted the glacier from one cirque to overflow into the next, enlarging the basin progressively downstream from the highest accumulation zone below Yr Wyddfa in a staircase sequence. The precise formation sequence is obscure, but the Glaslyn cirque glacier probably formed first as the ELA descended on Snowdon. Glaslyn possesses an almost perfectly semi-circular basin, with a spectacular riegel barring its exit and impounding a deep lake. The headway plunges 450m at more than 50° below Yr Wyddfa, continuing 39m below lake level. The rock barrier is 55m above the lake, falling eastwards where it is breached by the outlet stream. It slopes inwards at 30°, plastered with till and perched blocks, and outwards at 55-60° overhanging Cwm Llydaw by 220m. Basal ice excavating the cirque floor had to climb 94m with a strongly rotational flow pattern to abrade the rock barrier as it escaped Glaslyn. The considerable power of Glaslyn ice extended beyond formation of the rock basin and barrier; heavily abraded rock surfaces more than 120m above the barrier (still mirror-smooth in places), and the scarcity of moraine, testify to intense glacial scour.

Glaslyn ice flowed down-valley and began to excavate Cwm Llydaw, which became an accumulation zone itself as the ELA fell from 820m in Glaslyn to c. 620m, concentrated below Y Lliwedd. The combined glacier excavated an undulating basin for almost 2km along east-north-east fractures. The western lake basin is deepest (57m) where compressive flow enhanced erosion below a developing Glaslyn icefall. A submerged riegel 15-20m high lies 600m from the south-west shore with a second basin 45m below lake level to the east; this shallows to 3m near the Causeway, with a final 15m deep basin at the east end. Ice-abraded surfaces abound with good

**Photo 9: Crib Goch overlooking the entrance to Llanberis Pass (right).**
*Ice leaving the Snowdon Horseshoe (left) was swept into the Llanberis outlet trough severely truncating this east face of Snowdon. Photo: Ken Addison.*

examples visible at low water near the Causeway. A smaller, Upper Glaslyn glacier developed subsequently on Glaslyn's north-west wall, taking advantage of the parent basin as the ELA rose – possibly during the Loch Lomond Stadial – and excavating a small basin behind an abraded threshold 180m above lake level.

Substantial moraines are found only in the largest Snowdon cirques. Rapid ice-flow, encouraged by outward-sloping floor profiles, swept debris continuously from the small cirques above Llanberis Pass, leaving small moraines on retreat. Multiple moraine ridges – probably all of late-glacial age – are found in Clogwyn (Photo 10), Du'r Arddu, Tregalan and Llydaw. The Llydaw-Glaslyn glacier marked a terminus by an irregular elongated morainic arc 1.9km long, enclosing the eastern half of Llyn Llydaw. Till thickens into a huge ridge 35m high, extending into the lake from the north shore and continuing as a myriad hummocks on the opposite shore around the lake outlet. Fluctuating water levels have eroded those nearest to the lake and submerged others. Collectively, the south shore moraines and artificial weir impound a slightly higher lake level than the rock basins themselves.

The altitude of abraded rock surfaces indicates that ice over 400m thick occupied the Horseshoe in the Late Devensian; we may ask where this ice went, and when? The basin opens eastwards close to a col between three main valleys and the Gwryd valley (north-east) was the most direct route for the developing glacier. However, Llydaw ice at its thickest was swept into the Llanberis Pass by a transfluent outlet glacier (see Figure 11). High, abraded rock surfaces and thin till show that the east face of Crib Goch was torn off by ice flowing *north* from

*Photo 10: Late Devensian cirque glaciers excavated the compound rock basin of Cwm Clogwyn on Snowdon's west flank, leaving behind a series of small lakes and moraines. Photo: Ken Addison.*

Llydaw, overtopping Bwlch y Moch (180m above the bedrock floor of Llydaw) by at least 240m. Only a great force could have diverted the glacier through more than 90° and maximum development of Llydaw ice is thus correlated with the maximum extent of the Welsh ice sheet. As it retreated, Llydaw glacier resumed its easterly course, discharging into Nant Gwynant. Moraines in east Llydaw are attributed to the Loch Lomond Stadial when Llydaw-Glaslyn ice formed the largest cirque glacier in Snowdonia, which had disappeared by 9930 +/-120 years BP according to the oldest organic sediments amongst the lakeside moraines.

Nivation ornamented higher slopes extensively during the late-glacial. Many cirques contain small debris ridges, close in and parallel to rockwalls, in positions which make it more likely that they are protalus ramparts than moraines. Most are well inside Loch Lomond Stadial ice limits, particularly in Clogwyn (photo 10), Du'r Arddu and Tregalan and pre-date that stadial but others lie outside these limits, most notably in Cwm Dyli, and are harder to date. Nivation

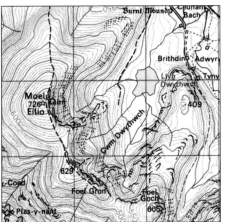

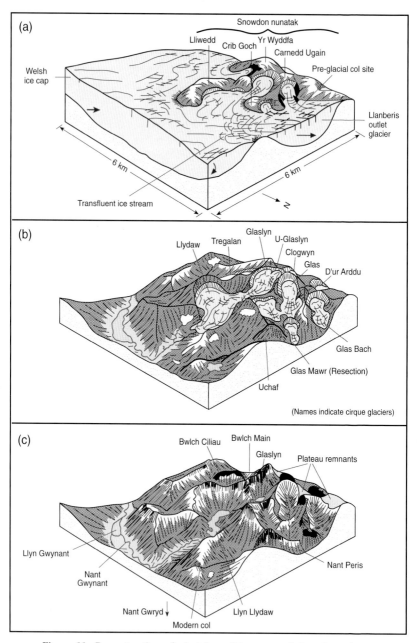

*Figure 11: Reconstruction of glacial conditions around Snowdon, showing the probable appearance of glaciers at (a) Late Devensian maximum (about 18 000 BP), (b) Loch Lomond Advance (about 11 000 BP) and (c) at the present time.*

was most extensive in the Moel Eilio ridge c.5km north-west of Yr Wyddfa, where lower elevations in relation to Devensian ELAs precluded substantial glacier development. Permanent snowbeds coalesced in gullies along a 4km north-east front, forming **nivation cirques** and eventually small cirque glaciers in Cwm Dwythwch. From lacustrine sediments in Llyn Dwythwch, it is clear that the climate at this altitude (less than 300m OD) was insufficiently severe for a glacier to reform in the Loch Lomond Stadial. A classic basal 'sandwich' of biogenic mud between two layers of minerogenic clay represents a late-glacial sequence of two severe-climate, solifluction-dominated sedimentation phases separated by a short climatic amelioration which permitted park tundra to colonise the cirque. Earlier minerogenic and organic sediments would have been swept out had a Loch Lomond Stadial glacier formed, as they were in Cwm Llydaw.

Snowdon cirques show important distinctions compared with the northern Glyderau cirques. The pattern of mountain glaciation was more diverse, temporally and spatially, and cirque glaciers were less sensitive to climate and eroded regardless of lithological differences. Rock basin enlargement permitted more accumulation and gave glaciers some control over their destiny, with the deep Glaslyn-Llydaw rock basins reflecting mature forms. Having nourished glaciers thick enough to deflect the Welsh ice sheet, Snowdon is an impressive monument to prolonged cirque glaciation.

## Access

Three main routes give access to all described sites. The Pyg Track offers an excellent panorama of the Llanberis Pass ascending from the car park at Pen-y-Pass (SH 647556) to Bwlch y Moch (SH 633553) (1.6km; around 1 hour). The Horseshoe unfolds during an easy climb below Crib Goch to a point above the Glaslyn barrier (3.1km; 1½hours) where it meets the Miners' Track (SH 615548 – 3.8km; 2 hours). The route steepens through Upper Glaslyn, zig-zagging to the summit plateau (4.8km; 3 hours) where it turns south beside the mountain railway to Yr Wyddfa (5.5km; 3½ hours). Unless taking the Snowdon Ranger Path, a return via the Miners' Track skirts Glaslyn and gives excellent views of the Glaslyn barrier and Llydaw moraines (5.5km; 2 hours).

The Miners' Track from Pen-y-Pass to the Causeway (SH 634548) rewards the less experienced (2.7km; 1 hour) and can be continued to Glaslyn (4.6km; 2 hours). The Snowdon Ranger Path from the Youth Hostel (SH 565551) east of Llyn Cwellyn is less demanding and offers views of Cwm Clogwyn and Llyn Du'r Arddu from Bwlch Cwm Brwynog (SH 591557 – 3.5km, 1½ hours) and during the ascent of Clogwyn Du'r Arddu to the summit (6.4km; 3 hours). Cloud is common above 750m and no walk on Snowdon should be attempted without proper clothing and footwear.

# THE LLANBERIS PASS

The Pass and twin lakes of Llanberis have attracted no more complete descriptions than Sir Andrew Ramsay's, written between 1852 and 1878. On Ramsay's death Professor Geikie wrote in 1892 'Among the most remarkable of his contributions to science are his papers that deal with glacial phenomena' and as the eye is drawn upwards by awesome rockwalls and enclosing summits it is easy to see what inspired Ramsay. His work included artistic reconstructions of '... the great glacier which descended the Pass of Llanberis' and he was convinced by 1855 that:

> 'ice attained its greatest thickness, perhaps at the very time when the Swiss and Himalayan glaciers were on a much grander scale than at present. At this period, in Wales, the glaciers, as proved by the groovings, passed straight across the tributary valleys of the Pass of Llanberis to a height of about 1300 feet above the floor of the main valley.'

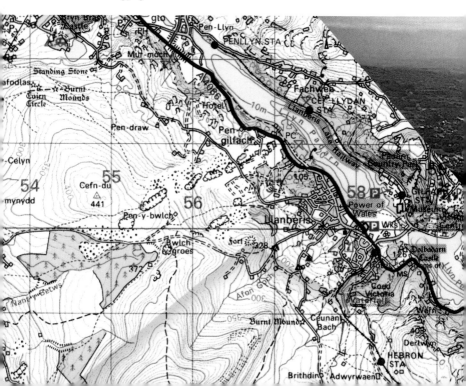

The 'Pass' incorporates the narrow trough extending 6km from Pen-y-Pass to Llyn Peris and the 8km rock basin containing Llyn Peris and Llyn Padarn (see Figure 12 and Photo 11).

## Nant Peris glacial breach

Although neither as wide nor as deep as Nant Ffrancon, Nant Peris breaches the Snowdon-Glyderau plateau more abruptly than its counterpart. With less opportunity on Snowdon's north-west ridge for cirque glaciers to open out the valley, the trough underwent only minor alpine modification after excavation by transfluent ice. Its canyon-like form led many to believe that this and similar valleys were, paradoxically, ravines incised by rejuvenated rivers prior to glaciation. This belief discounted the Davis theory of major glacial erosion around Snowdon and disregards two fundamental features of the troughs: Nant Peris, Nant Ffrancon and two further troughs breach the 15km mountain axis south-west of Pen yr Ole Wen, whereas there are none in 25km north-east through the Carneddau. Such an anomaly is unlikely under fluvial origins and Nant Peris possesses classic signs of glacial breaching.

Pen-y-Pass marks the modern watershed at 359m OD, but surviving plateau remnants at Gyrn Las and Esgair Felen suggest that it once lay 3km to the west, close to the structural axis between Yr Wyddfa and Glyder Fawr. These opposing cliffs, breached at 850m OD and 790m OD respectively, directly above the valley floor at 160m OD, indicate

*Photo 11: The lower Llanberis rock basin is occupied now by Llyn Peris (foreground) and Llyn Padarn (background).* Photo: Ken Addison.

a maximum glacial excavation of 690m. Rock surfaces reveal intense glacial scour and, as Ramsay observed, two directions of ice-flow. Dominant older striations cut across tributary cirques north-westwards, parallel to the valley, and point to the Migneint source of Welsh ice rather than Snowdon; fresher striations high on the south flank point to ice emanating later from north Snowdon cirques. Llydaw ice was deflected around Crib Goch into Nant Peris during maximum glaciation, and striations show that contemporaneous Glas and Uchaf cirque glaciers were also swept into the developing transfluent trough.

The Glas Mawr and Glas Bach cirques were formed after the trough in a manner reminiscent of the northern Glyderau cirques (Figure 9 on page 31). Both are about 250m lower than Uchaf and Glas with striations pointing north and north-east, contrary to those aligned with main valley ice-flow on severely abraded arêtes above Dinas Mot (SH 625562), Clogwyn Mawr and below Llechog (SH 606567). Their sites, situated close to the pre-glacial watershed, required opening up before localised accumulation could develop. Furthermore, Glas Mawr represents the lower basin of a cirque staircase. With ice overflowing the rock step from Glas and Uchaf, it may have held a resection glacier, ie. a glacier with no independent accumulation zone and fed instead by avalanching from the icefall, examples of which occur in similar topographic locations in Alaska today.

It is likely that an outlet glacier from the Welsh ice sheet excavated Nant Peris, exploiting north-west to south-east fractures, 18 000 years ago; a diffluent lobe about 100m thick overflowed the col into Cwm Idwal. The apparent confluence of some Snowdon cirque glaciers with the Welsh ice sheet, and the similarity of their mean ELA of 835m OD on Snowdon with 793m OD for the highest Glyder cirques, suggests that they were contemporaneous. Judging from abraded spur elevations the outlet glacier had a surface slope of 9-10°; its rapid discharge, and that of later valley and cirque glaciers, ensured the dominance of ice-scoured surfaces. Indeed, apart from small Loch Lomond Stadial cirque moraines, till is scarce and confined to a veneer which thickens occasionally near the valley floor, especially upstream of large roches moutonnées above Pont y Gromlech (SH 630565) and Ynys Ettws (SH 622568). Ice-flow was sufficiently retarded by bedrock humps to release and then streamline basal till. Perched blocks are a major feature of the valley, located where they could not have fallen from adjacent cliffs.

Nant Peris exhibits a classic U-shaped profile and again there is some evidence of a lesser trough in the valley floor. Ledges leading to the roches moutonnées above Pont y Gromlech and Ynys Ettws in particular overhang the floor by 45-50m and their truncated outer slopes may represent final excavation by the valley glacier, fed by overhanging cirques and residual flow from Llydaw. Evidence of this glacier is also found in lacustrine sediments, described below. Glaciation concluded with small Loch Lomond Stadial cirque glaciers, but the effects of glacial destabilisation of precipitous rockwalls lasted into modern times. The most impressive block scree is found between Pen-y-Pass and Pont y Gromlech and the largest individual boulders, the size of small houses, lie beneath Dinas Gromlech (SH 628567).

# The Peris-Padarn rock basin

The outlet glacier gained in erosive power as it accelerated and steepened through the trough, gouging out the depths of the valley floor as effectively as it breached the mountain heights. Directed at the valley floor, it excavated an undulating rock basin over 8km long from Gwastadnant to Cwm-y-glo, still occupied by lakes (see Figure 12). Llyn Peris (1.8km long) was separated from Llyn Padarn (3.2km) by the post-glacial Afon Arddu fan delta at Pont-y-Bala, its original shape further modified by Dinorwic quarry spoil and its modern function as the lower reservoir for the Dinorwic pumped storage hydro-electric scheme. Lake soundings, boreholes and direct observations reveal that the basin was most deeply excavated nearest the breach and shallows down-valley. At least 27m of delta sediments overlie bedrock at the Peris lakehead – only 35m OD – and the lake is 55m deep, compared with maximum known depths of 27m and 24m in the upper and middle sections of Padarn. If basin depth is

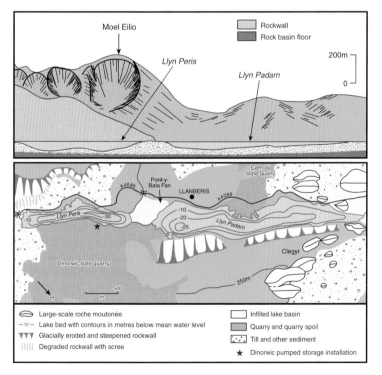

*Figure 12: The Peris-Padarn rock basin.*
*The ridge of Moel Eilio and small cirques surrounding Cwm Dwythwch lie 3km south-west beyond the lakes.*

difficult to appreciate visually, severely abraded surfaces and huge roches moutonnées reflect the enormous erosive power of ice, especially on hard Pre-Cambrian tuffs above the east shore of Padarn at Clegyr. Llyn Peris was drained for construction work during 1975, exposing unweathered, deeply grooved and abraded rock surfaces protruding through lake-bed sediments. Many striations slope upstream at 5-10°, indicating rotational flow in basal ice.

Sediments filling remaining parts of the basin, particularly in the Llyn Peris lakehead and Pont-y-Bala fans, tell the late-glacial and post-glacial history of the valley (see Figure 6). Basal **rhythmites** more than 27m thick record prolonged deep-water lacustrine sedimentation for about 800 years after the basin became ice-free, although microscopic surface textures of sand grains and overlying glaciofluvial deposits show that glaciers were still present in upper Nant Peris. The first organic horizons were found in the Pont-y-Bala fan and reach 20m thick at the Peris lakehead, yielding macrofossils and pollen indicative of the tundra environment also found in Nant Ffrancon and a radiocarbon date of 11 260 (+/-200 years) BP. Thereafter woodland progressively colonised the valley; a pine/birch/hazel community dated at 9400 (+/-200 years) BP was eventually replaced by a mixed oak woodland about 6500 years ago. Unlike Nant Ffrancon, the surviving lakes record environmental changes into the modern period, aided by the Pont-y-Bala fan which began to develop during Late Devensian deglaciation. Thick peat accumulation in Nant Peris is attributed to the fan's effect in damming and deepening Llyn Peris.

It is fitting to conclude by recording that Ramsay developed the first theories on glacial origins of rock basin lakes with the Llanberis Pass, *inter alia,* very much in mind. Many formative processes on the Llanberis lake basins are implicit in his explanations of 1862:

'It required a solid body [of ice], grinding steadily and powerfully in direct and heavy contact with and across the rocks, to scoop out deep hollows, the situations of which might be determined by unequal hardness of rock, by extra weight of ice ...'

and in 1878:

'In the region of the Alps it is a remarkable circumstance that all the large lakes lie in the direct channels of the great old glaciers – each lake in a true rock-basin.'

## Access

The A4086 from Caernarfon to Capel Curig runs through the Pass, providing access with small lay-bys as excellent vantage points. Those along the south shores of Llyn Padarn and Llyn Peris, and below Dinas y Gromlech (SH 628567) afford magnificent views of the breach and specific local features. Scrambles into the cirques, especially Glas Mawr (SH 619564), provide good panoramas and similar views are obtained (with care) from above the south flank rockwalls, with mountain access via a minor road 130m south-east of the Mountain Railway terminus (SH 583597).

# REGIONAL GLACIATION OF SNOWDONIA

## Devensian Cold Stage environments

Key landforms have been studied so far but, since the full extent of Snowdonia's glacial heritage is beyond the scope of this book, we conclude with a synopsis of regional glaciation and other areas worth exploring. With improved understanding of Late Quaternary environments, it becomes possible and preferable to develop dynamic models of glacial activity, constrained by more realistic dates. The sites described so far are also pieces of a puzzle which cannot be totally isolated from any other landform of Snowdonia, nor the glaciers which formed them. The most realistic models link glaciers and landforms genetically in glacio-morphological **landsystems**. However, since we were not present to see them develop, our models are best estimates which rely on informed, state-of-the-art interpretations of events and modern glacier research.

North Wales glaciers are implicated in several British glaciations during the past 0.7 million years through the wide distribution of Snowdonian erratics in the southern Irish Sea basin, South Wales, the English Midlands and Thames basin. Earlier traces in Snowdonia were altered beyond current recognition by repeated, subsequent glaciation and our best-developed models so far cover no more than the Devensian Cold Stage. The last temperate stage (Ipswichian) was terminated by an abrupt climatic deterioration c.115 000 BP, after which the north European region experienced rapid fluctuations between stadial and interstadial conditions during the Early Devensian until c.80 000 BP.

At least two such interstadial episodes are recorded in biogenic sediments from fossil river channels at Pen-y-bryn, Caernarfon; an earlier, coniferous forest environment was replaced after a significant interval by a tundra/forest ecotone (ecosystem transition) (Photos 12 and 13). In [14]C terms these episodes occurred c.60 000 and 40 000 BP respectively. However, these are *minimum* ages and, by modern convention, are correlated with less cold **Oxygen Isotope.** Substages 5c and 5a at c.100 000 and 80 000 BP (see Figure 1); preliminary uranium series dating tends to confirm these older ages.

Welsh Till capping these organic beds was deposited by a glacier advancing from north-west Snowdon, bulldozing trees in its path. This is the first substantial evidence for an Early Devensian glacial stage in Wales at c.75 000 BP. It was probably modest in extent and shortlived, terminated by more severe and sustained arid cold in the Middle Devensian, when the Atlantic polar fronts migrated south of

*Photo 12: A shallow, abandoned river channel lined with peat in a working quarry at Pen-y-bryn (out of bounds to the public). These are overlain in turn by light grey, Early Devensian till, and brown, Late Devensian glaciofluvial gravels. Photo: Ken Addison.*

*Photo 13: Highly compressed organic-rich sediments at Pen-y-bryn provide vital evidence of boreal forest conditions, dated to the Early Devensian and providing a maximum age for the ovelying glacial till. Photo: Ken Addison.*

Britain and permafrost became the dominant geomorphic agent. Nevertheless, the minimum size of the glacier – extending 10-12km from west Snowdon to Caernarfon – testifies to local alpine glaciation in Snowdonia at this time, requiring a reappraisal of Late Pleistocene landscape evolution.

The Devensian saved its most dramatic events to the last, with the global growth and decay of major ice sheets between 26 000-10 000 BP. It is to this Late Devensian glacial stage that we still attribute the greater part of Snowdonia's glacial geomorphic landsystem. Even as the evidence for earlier glaciers in the landscape is pieced together and investigated further, the hard evidence is that extensive ice from an inland Welsh source swept most of the region immediately prior to temperate episodes of Late Devensian interstadial or early Holocene age. The following event sequence and chronology is suggested.

Small cirque glaciers began to form on the highest mountain summits after 26 000 BP as the ELA fell below 900m, some at least coalescing to form alpine valley glaciers. Continued ELA lowering eventually established the Welsh ice sheet whose radial outflow breached the Snowdonia watershed most dramatically in the Snowdon-Glyderau and Glyderau-Carneddau cols. Hemispheric ice sheets reached their maximum extent by 18 000 BP, at which time Welsh ice reached an estimated maximum surface elevation of 1400m in the Migneint-Arenig region. Its radial outflow, traced by erratic trails and regional striation patterns, overran Snowdonia to the north-west, engulfing the alpine glaciers and joining a major, south-moving glacier in the Irish Sea basin – which had drained as sea-levels fell during englaciation.

The British ice sheet appears to have wasted more rapidly than it developed and the modern coast in southern Snowdonia was ice free by 14 150 BP. For a time, local mountain glaciation entered a more effective period, exploiting the breaches. Despite evidence for earlier alpine glaciation, cirques were developed extensively during the last stages of Devensian glaciation, between 18 000 and 10 000 years BP. The densest cirque concentrations in Snowdonia occur in the troughs of Nant Ffrancon and Llanberis Pass. The Carneddau has a larger area above 500m OD than the rest of Snowdonia combined, yet cirques occupy only 10% of this area, compared with over 48% in the Glyderau; there are no glacial breaches in the Carneddau. Immature morphology and the steeply out-sloping floors of most cirques indicates the pre-existence of deep troughs, opening up the plateau as a prerequisite to extensive cirque development. Trough and cirque development therefore were spatially, if not temporally, closely interrelated.

Cirque glaciers fed short valley glaciers radiating from Snowdon, Glyder Fawr and Carnedd Llewelyn until c.12 000 BP, in the Older Dryas part of the Late Devensian late-glacial, after rapid warming (Allerød, see page 15) which may have caused the temporary disappearance of glaciers. However, the Devensian cold stage had one last fling when over 30 Loch Lomond Stadial cirque glaciers reformed in the Younger Dryas, between 11 125-9400 BP.

## Late Devensian glacier and geomorphic landsystems

The impact of successive glaciers, translated into recognisable geomorphic landsystems, was segregated spatially in a way which allows us to reconstruct the former *glacier* landsystems. Four distinct landsystem zones are recognised (Figure 13); note, with caution, the dependence of one reconstruction on the other and the blurring of zone boundaries as the ice sheet expanded and contracted across the same ground (Figure 14).

## Zone 1: Ice centre landsystem

Erosional features may be inconspicuous and glacigenic sediment sparse in ice sheet accumulation areas. Zero or low basal velocities and little meltwater in 'polar' ice centres considerably reduce quarrying and abrasion rates and generate little debris. Moreover, polar ice buries the entire landscape, erosion is more uniformly distributed and only **nunataks** provide scope for undercutting and supra-glacial debris.

The Late Devensian Welsh Ice Sheet was centred in the Migneint Plateau, with an ice divide running north-south near Llyn Conwy (SH 780460) and Carnedd Iago (SH 783407), 25km south-east of a centre once believed to focus on Snowdon. The monotonous plateau surface, seen from the B4407, is typical of former ice centres in Scandinavia with scant evidence of traditional glacial landforms.

Thin till, confined to valley floors and frequently peat covered, contains only local bedrock material, much of which (eg. Ordovician Garth Grit and Clogwyn Hir tuff) provides indicator erratics in tills tens of kilometres north and west. Welsh till derived from Lower Palaeozoic rocks is blue-grey in colour, weathering to olive. Exposed bedrock surfaces are extensively abraded (although weathered), separated by shallow rock basin lakes or peat bogs, with good examples around Llyn Conwy. To the east lie the Arenig mountains

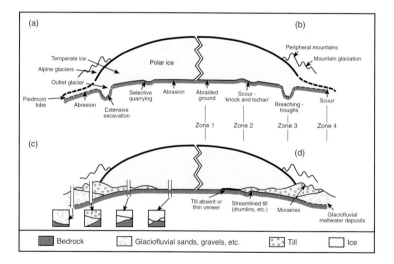

**Figure 13: Principal features of ice sheet glaciation.**
*(a) erosive processes and glacier types, (b) erosional landforms, (c) stratigraphy, (d) sedimentary landforms. Zones refer to areas of Snowdonia identified in the text and on Figure 14.*

and other peaks, which were the source of indicator erratics in the West Midlands. Submerged by up to 1000m of ice at glacial maximum, they emerged as nunataks during early deglaciation and supported small, east-facing Loch Lomond Stadial cirque glaciers. In advanced stages of deglaciation, Migneint ice lobes stagnated on lower ground and kame terraces mark their margins with massive examples straddling the A5 south-east from Betwys-y-coed near Pentrefoelas (SH 877515).

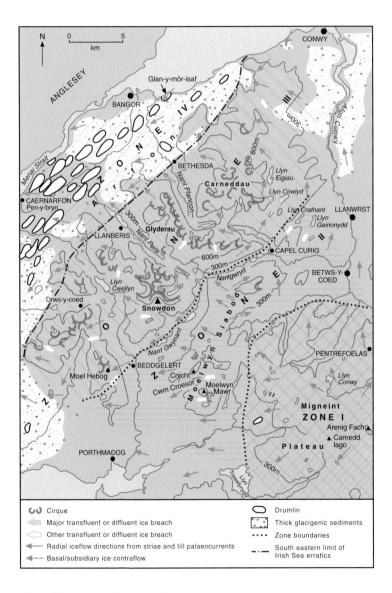

*Figure 14: Regional glaciation of Snowdonia.*

## Zone 2: Selective erosion landsystem

Away from ice dispersal centres, ice selectively eroded bedrock channels and sedimentation became more widespread. In the Moelwyn-Siabod range, flanking the Migneint Plateau 12km to the west, till is still scarce and only three cirques are found on isolated peaks but signs of basal scour are everywhere and there is evidence that basal ice began to 'stream' at depth, eroding distinctive channels. The plateau displays knock-and-lochan topography (lake-filled rock basins amongst roche moutonnées and scoured rock bosses) but at Cwm Croesor (SH 645455) a trough over 420m deep was excavated between Moelwyn Mawr (SH 659449) and Cnicht (SH 645465). There are no adjacent cirques which might have nourished a Croesor valley glacier, but its convex head, with abraded ground littered with more than a dozen rock-basin lakes, is indicative of accelerating basal ice. Llyn Crafnant (SH 750610) and Llyn Geirionydd (SH 763610), at least l9m and 13m deep respectively, occupy rock basins in smaller troughs in similar topographic locations where Zone 2 extends into the eastern Carneddau. All three troughs are aligned north-east to south-west whereas the general radial ice-flow was to the north and west; there is no glaciological objection to this, since basal ice is guided by the underlying relief while ice several hundred metres above is not, and contraflow is common within modern ice sheets.

The Gwynant-Gwryd through-valley from Beddgelert (SH 590480) to Capel Curig (SH 720580) is also aligned north-east to south-west and forms the Zone 2-3 boundary. Preglacial valleys probably existed here and Snowdon ice further deepened both branches; however, the valleys also discharged basal ice unable to override the mountains immediately to the west. *Upper* ice, high in the Welsh ice sheet, breached the mountains but *basal* ice met the solid mountain wall and could not escape to the north-west. Instead, it was extruded south-west around Moel Hebog (SH 565469) and north-east around the Carneddau massif. The Croesor, Crafnant and Geirionydd troughs were probably repercussions of the same basal ice jam, and all troughs were excavated more easily along the principal Caledonian fractures. The Cowlyd breach in the Carneddau provides the most convincing evidence for basal ice deflection; Llyn Cowlyd occupied a natural rock basin 55m deep, and the total depth of 490m carved through the heart of Pen Llithrig y Wrach (SH 716623) could not have occurred, as Dury suggested, as a result of an obstructed Idwal-Bochlwyd valley glacier. The Cowlyd breach and Migneint-sourced till at c. 1000m OD in the Carneddau indicate the passage of very thick ice, and Cowlyd is aligned with the deflected basal ice route as it crossed the Cefn Capel ridge (SH 700581) 2km west of Capel Curig.

## Zone 3: Outlet glacier landsystem

The full impact of the Welsh Ice Sheet was felt towards its margin. Ice entered its ablation zone, transforming towards a 'temperate' thermodynamic state, and accelerated, excavating large bedrock channels – especially where its outflow was barred by the Snowdonia Mountains. Since they are the focus of this book, little more need be said here on this zone. Apart from Nant Ffrancon and Nant Peris, troughs 490m and 435m deep respectively were excavated at Drws-y-coed (SH 545535) and Nant-y-Betws (SH 550557); both have associated rock basins and Llyn Cwellyn (over 34m deep) occupies the latter. They lie west of Snowdon, where Snowdon ice (from Cwm Clogwyn) was probably drawn into the main ice-stream. Incipient breaches, diffluent cols and other signs of general overriding ice all point to the same escape of ice over and around the Hebog group. Independent cirque and valley glaciation preceded and followed maximum glaciation in the Hebog and Carneddau groups as elsewhere; eight cirques line the ridge between Mynydd Graig Goch (SH 497485) and Y Garn (SH 552526) and eleven lie close to the main Carneddau ridge. Throughout Zone 3, Loch Lomond Stadial cirque moraines are the most distinctive forms of glacial deposition, although older till veneer and perched erratic blocks are widespread.

## Zone 4: Glacier confluence and piedmont landsystem

Increased basal and sidewall erosion in the mountains resulted in increased deposition at and beyond the ice-margin, modified by considerable quantities of meltwater. In the Arfon Lowlands **piedmont zone** beyond the mountains, a large volume of ice moving south through the Irish Sea basin became confluent with Welsh ice, probably before glacial maximum c.20 000 BP. From the distribution of Irish Sea basin erratics (including Lake District and Scottish rocks) and glacio-tectonic (ice-generated deformation) structures in sediments from both sources, the confluence appears to have migrated across Arfon and Anglesey; no Irish Sea ice sediments are found south-east of a line of cols from Bethesda (SH 625665) through Llanberis (SH 577600) to Nantlle (SH 510534). **Drumlins** are aligned south-westwards parallel to the combined ice-flow in the countryside around Caernarfon (SH 480625) and Bethel (SH 524653). Some are more than 1km long and up to 45m high, but most are rock-cored rather than pure debris accumulations. A fluvioglacial melt-out complex with individual **eskers** and **kames** can be seen at Pentir (SH 573670) and multiple tills at Pen-y-bryn (Seiont Quarry, SH 490615). Marine erosion exposes good but unstable sections in glacigenic deposits near Glan-y-môr-isaf (SH 622727) (Photo 14) and particularly along the coast south-west of Anglesey at Dinas Dinlle (SH 435563).

The dynamics of glacier sedimentation in the piedmont zone are the subject of great contemporary interest, concerning not only ice confluence behaviour but also a possible glaciomarine event. The great variability in sediment type and source, clear evidence of deformation during/after deposition and the occasional presence of arctic marine shells *may* point to a catastrophic collapse of the western British ice sheet. The argument goes that, although sea-level fell due to global glacial advance, this was partially counter-acted by ice sheet depression of the local crust. Then, on deglaciation, the sea

*Photo 14: Interlocking clays and sands of Welsh Ice (grey, olive) and Irish Sea Ice (red) origin at Glan-y-môr-isaf.*
Photo: Ken Addison.

flooded back into the Irish Sea basin faster than initial ice retreat. The ice margin began to float as an ice shelf, leading first to accelerated ice loss through iceberg calving and then causing the ice sheet behind to *surge* forward as its frontal support collapsed. The drumlin field in Arfon and Anglesey and thrust-faulting visible in coastal exposures are thought by some to indicate surging glacier behaviour. Withdrawal of the Irish Sea ice may have also allowed a temporary resurgence of Welsh outlet glaciers, fanning out as piedmont lobes. Although this is not yet proven, it is an intriguing proposition that there may be geomorphic evidence around Snowdonia from the Late Devensian for the sort of ice shelf/ice sheet decoupling we are concerned about in the Antarctic today.

Through all four zones, Snowdonia provides a magnificent display of glacial landforms rarely found in such a compact area and illustrative of such a wide array of glacial geomorphic processes.

# ACCESS
# AND SAFETY

The location and access map (Figure 15) should help any visitor to the area to plan tours and fieldwork to Snowdonia to their best advantage. This provides an overview of the area studied and will put the processes discussed in the previous chapters into perspective.

## Access

Most land in Snowdonia is in private ownership. The rules of access applying to the countryside apply just as rigorously to areas of outstanding beauty and popularity, such as National Parks. Visitors are asked to observe the *Country Code*, the *Geologist's Code of Conduct* and the interests of the Countryside Council for Wales, Snowdonia National Park Authority and National Trust.

Large areas of Snowdonia are also designated National Nature Reserves, Sites of Special Scientific Interest or National Trust Areas. They possess distinctive and often rare flora and fauna; suffer considerable visitor pressures; are susceptible to severe footpath erosion and are generally sensitive to human influences. Visitors are asked especially to observe the following specific requests:

- keep to footpaths where available, especially where they have been reinforced, re-routed, etc., to reduce erosion hazards;
- collect rock and sediment samples sensitively; restrict rock samples to unweathered blocks fallen from outcrops;
- do not collect wild flowers, or disturb wildlife; it may be unlawful to do so and certainly threatens rare species;
- groups of visitors, school parties for instance, should explore away from footpaths only with prior consent from the owner;
- group leaders should inform Countryside Council for Wales if its reserves are to be visited and check if permits are required;
- group leaders should make prior contact with the **Youth and Schools Liaison Officer** at the **Snowdonia National Park Office**, Penrhyndeudraeth, Gwynedd LL48 6LF (tel 01766 770274).

These requests are intended to ensure that access is beneficial to all concerned, rather than restrictive; the various agencies are excellent sources of useful information, augmented by the **National Museum of Wales (tel 01286 870630)** and **Oriel Eryryi (First Hydro) (tel 01286 870636).**

## Safety

'Mountaineering' accidents usually involve people who are ill-equipped, stretched beyond the limits of their experience or physical condition, or unaware of how rapidly mountain weather can

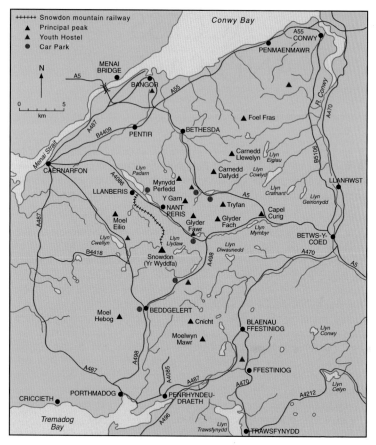

*Figure 15: Location and access to Snowdonia.*

deteriorate. Accidents are avoidable if sensible precautions are taken.

Temperatures can fall in still air at 1°C per 100m of ascent, and increased exposure to winds as summits are approached considerably reduces effective temperatures due to wind-chill. Fine weather can give way to thick cloud and heavy rain or snow in less than 1 hour, and summits often experience Arctic conditions. **Mountaincall Snowdonia (tel 0891 500449)** provides detailed forecasts, including cloud base, freezing levels and summit temperatures. For site visibility and safety, ascertain the forecast *cloud base* for the duration of visits using higher routes. Watch for deteriorating weather and return to lower ground if in doubt.

Appropriate clothing is essential, including boots or other stout footwear and adequate warm, waterproof clothing, even if the weather is fine (exposure or bad sprains are avoidable, but often involve Mountain Rescue services). Carry spare clothing, torch, whistle, first aid kit, emergency food and a 'space blanket' and/or survival bag. Higher routes should not be attempted in winter without equipment for, and experience of, snow and ice conditions.

# GLOSSARY

**Arête** A narrow, precipitous mountain ridge representing the residual divide between adjoining *cirque* basins and frequently serrated by frost action.

**BP** Before the Present; age based on radiocarbon ($^{14}$C) dates before the base year AD1950.

**Biostratigraphy** Differentiation of sediment (or rock) units through their included biotic remains, which may also indicate environmental conditions at the time of incorporation and be suitable for radiometric dating; remains may be microfossils (pollen grains, diatoms, etc.) or macrofossils (plant stems, leaves seeds, bones or whole organisms, etc.).

**Cirque** A deep recess in a mountainous upland formed by the erosive processes of a small, individual glacier and usually possessing some or all of the following: oversteepened retaining walls; gently inclined floor, with a rock barrier *(threshold)* sometimes forming a rock basin; morainic debris in the form of a ridge across the exit; signs of glacial scour and quarrying.

**Devensian** The Late Pleistocene, and most recent, cold stage in British terminology, extending from c.115 000-10 000 BP; synonymous with the European *Weichselian.*

**Diffluent trough** A trough eroded by the lateral branch of a glacier through an adjacent pre-glacial divide.

**Drumlin** A large-scale glacigenic landform of *till* and glacio-fluvial units, forming a low hill elongated in the direction of flow with a blunt upstream end, streamlined by overriding ice. Diffluent trough. A trough eroded by the lateral branch of a glacier through an adjacent pre-glacial divide.

**Erratic** A rock fragment carried by a glacier and deposited beyond the rock outcrop from which it was derived, rendering it distinctive from underlying bedrock.

**Esker** A long, narrow mound composed mainly of dislocated, stratified, glaciofluvial sediments, having been deposited formerly in an ice-walled channel and representing the cast of an en-glacial or sub-glacial stream.

**Flandrian** The current *temperate stage* of global climate which commenced c.10 000 BP, based stratigraphically on the post-glacial rise in sea-level in the English Channel area.

**Glaciomarine** Referring to a glacial subsystem of tidewater glaciers, ice shelves and icebergs which assumes considerable importance in our understanding of past and present glaciation. Glaciers and ice sheets entering the sea float when water depth approximately equals ice thickness, strongly influencing their dynamics and behaviour.

**Holocene** The second and shorter epoch of the Quaternary period commencing c.10 000 BP; unsatisfactorily regarded as the post-glacial and preferably near-equivalent to the current Flandrian temperate stage.

**Icefall** The highly crevassed and rapidly moving section of a glacier flowing over a steep bedrock slope.

**Kame** An isolated hillock of collapsed, stratified glaciofluvial sediment.

**Kame terrace** A pitted, flat-topped terrace of stratified glaciofluvial sediments, deposited between a downwasting or stagnant ice lobe and adjacent valleyside, parallel to the ice-margin; the steep former ice-contact slope is dislocated as the ice melts.

**Landsystem** A large-scale landscape comprising a wide range of landforms genetically.

**Loch Lomond Stadial** The last event of the Late Devensian glacial stage, developing from ice-free conditions between c.11 000-10 000 BP in the western Scottish Highlands; small glaciers developed during this time elsewhere in Highland Britain, including Snowdonia.

**Moraine** A mound, ridge or other distinct accumulation of till deposited chiefly by ice, sometimes used to describe an amorphous veneer of till.

**Nivation** Processes of weathering and erosion beneath and at the margins of a snowpatch, chiefly by frost action, and the sliding, solifluction or meltwater transport of resultant debris.

**Nivation cirques** A deep recess in a mountainous upland, eroded by the combined processes of frost weathering and growth and decay of snowbeds, but lacking glacial ice and its geometric consequences.

**Nunatak** Inuit word meaning lonely peak, referring to an isolated rock outcrop projecting prominently through a glacier surface and entirely surrounded by ice.

**Oxygen Isotope stage** An events stratigraphy of cold and temperate stages identified from the isotopic composition of marine organisms, reflecting the fractionation of oxygen isotopes as water is taken up, or released, by ice sheets.

**Piedmont zone** A lobe of ice, spreading unconfined over a lowland as an outlet or other glacier emerges from a confined, mountain zone.

**Pleistocene** The first and longer epoch of the Quaternary period, ending c.10 000 years ago.

**Protalus rampart** A debris ridge formed at the lower margin of a snowpatch by nivation processes.

**Quaternary** The current geological period which began c.1.8 million years ago and is characterised by a procession of global cold and temperate stages.

**Rhythmite** An individual unit of a rhythmic sequence of sediments, in this case referring to varved clays with each varve representing several millimetres of coarser summer or finer winter sedimentation with an annual accumulation; the number of varves thus provides an estimate of the time span of deposition.

**Riegel** A bedrock step in the long profile of a glaciated valley, usually formed at an ice confluence or zone of differential bedrock resistance.

**Roche moutonnée** A small bedrock hillock sculptured by strong ice-flow; the upstream (stoss) end is typically smoothed by abrasion and the downstream (lee) slope is steep and irregular due to subglacial cavitation and quarrying.

**Striae/striation** Superficial scratches or furrows inscribed on underlying bedrock by debris-impregnated basal ice; not to be confused with structures in the rock.

**Till** A clastic sediment deposited beneath a glacier, replacing the term boulder clay, it indicates a heterogenous mix of rock and mineral fragments of varied lithological composition.

**Transfluent trough** A trough excavated by ice breaching a preglacial divide in the principal direction of movement of a major icestream.

# BIBLIOGRAPHY AND FURTHER READING

Addison, K. (1981) 'The contribution of discontinuous rock-mass failure to glacier erosion' in *Annals of Glaciology* 2, 3-10.

Addison, K. (1989) *The Ice Age in Y Glyderau and Nant Ffrancon.* Addison Landsystem Practice.

Addison, K., Edge, M.J. and Watkins, R. (eds) (1990) *The Quaternary of North Wales: Field Guide.* Quaternary Research Association, Coventry.

Addison, K. and Edge, M.J. (1992) 'Early Devensian interstadial and glacigenic sediments in Gwynedd, North Wales' in *Geological Journal* 27, 2, 181-90.

Addison, K. and Campbell, S. (1994) 'Conservation, access and land management conflict in upland glaciated areas of the Snowdonia National Park: a preliminary survey' in O'Halloran, D., Green, C., Harley M. and Knill, J. (eds) *Geological and Landscape Conservation,* 161-73. Geological Society and JNCC, London.

Bennett, M.R. (1989) *The cwms of Snowdonia: a morphometric analysis.* Research Paper 2, Department of Geography, Queen Mary and Westfield College, London University.

British Geological Survey Maps of Wales and the Welsh Borders are available as follows: 1:250 000 of Wales 1st edn; medium-scale (1:50 000) of: Llandudno, Bangor, Denbigh, Flint, Snowdon, Corwen, Wrexham, Aberdaron and Bardsey Island, Harlech, Bala, Oswestry, Wem, Cadair Idris, Aberystwyth, Montgomery, Church Stretton, Aberaeron, Llanilar, Rhayader, St David's, Milford, Haverfordwest, Carmarthen, Ammanford, Merthyr Tydfil, Abergavenny, Monmouth, Pembroke and Linney Head, Swansea, Pontypridd, Newport, Chepstow; medium-scale (1:63 360) of: Flint, Carmarthen, Worms Head, Swansea, Newport; a special monograph *Ordovician (caradoc) marginal basin volanism in Snowdonia,* 1991, ISBN 0 11 884465 2 and a field guide *Geological excursions in the Harlech Dome,* 1985, ISBN 0 11 884285 4 are also available. Catalogues for BGS resources are available from: Sales Desk, BGS, Kingsley Dunham Centre, Keyworth, Nottingham NG12 5GG. Tel: 0115 936 3241. Fax: 0115 936 3488.

Buckland, W. (1842) 'On the glacial-diluvial phenomena in Snowdonia and adjacent parts of North Wales' in *Proceedings of the Geological Society of London* 3, 2, 84, 579-84.

Campbell, S. and Bowen, D.Q. (1989) *Quaternary of Wales.* Geological Conservation Review, Nature Conservancy Council, Peterborough.

Darwin, C. (1842) 'Notes on the effects produced by the ancient glaciers of Caernarvonshire, and on boulders transported by floating ice' in *Philosophical Magazine* series 3, 21, 180-8.

Davis, W.M. (1909) 'Glacial erosion in North Wales' in *Quarterly Journal of the Geological Society of London* 65, 259, 281-350.

Dury, G.H. (1976) *The Face of the Earth.* Penguin, London.

Embleton, C. (1962) *British Landscapes Through Maps 5: Snowdonia.* The Geographical Association, Sheffield.

Gemmell, C., Smart, D. and Sugden, D. (1986) 'Striae and former ice-flow directions in Snowdonia, North Wales' in *Geographical Journal* 152, 1, 19-29.

Gray, J.M. (1982) 'The last glaciers (Loch Lomond Advance) in Snowdonia' in *Geological Journal* 17, 2, 111-33.

Howells, M.F., Leveridge, B.E. and Redman, A.J. (1981) *Snowdonia. A Geological Field Guide.* Unwin, London.

Ince, J. (1983) 'Two post-glacial pollen profiles from the uplands of Snowdonia, Gwynedd, North Wales' in *New Phytologist* 95, 159-72.

Pardoe, H.S. and Thomas, B.A. (1992) *Snowdon's Plants since the Glaciers.* National Museum of Wales, Cardiff.

Ramsay, A.C. (1855) 'On the thickness of the ice of the ancient glaciers of North Wales, and other points bearing on the glaciation of the country' in *Report of the British Association for 1854.* Sections 94-95.

Ramsay, A.C. (1860) *The Old Glaciers of Switzerland and North Wales.* Longman, London.

Ramsay, A.C. (1862) 'On the glacial origins of certain lakes in Switzerland, the Black Forest, Great Britain, Sweden, North America, and elsewhere' in *Quarterly Journal of the Geological Society of London* 18, 185-204.

Ramsay, A.C. (1878) *The Physical Geology and Geography of Great Britain* (fifth edition). Edward Standford, London.

Sharp, M., Dowdeswell, J.A. and Gemmell, J.C. (1989) 'Reconstructing past glacier dynamics from glacial geomorphic evidence: Snowdon, North Wales' in *Journal of Quaternary Science* 4, 2, 115-30.

Tinsley, H.M. and Derbyshire, E. (1976) 'Late-glacial and post-glacial sedimentation in the Peris-Padarn Rock Basins North Wales' in *Nature* 260, 234-8.

Tipping R. (1993) 'A detailed early post-glacial (Flandrian) pollen diagram from Cwm Idwal, North Wales' in *New Phytologist* 125, 175-91.

Unwin, D.J. (1973) 'The distribution and orientation of corries in northern Snowdonia, Wales' in *Transactions of the Institute of British Geographers* 58, 85-97.